The University of Wisconsin

PUBLICATIONS IN MEDIEVAL SCIENCE

PUBLICATIONS IN MEDIEVAL SCIENCE

1

The Medieval Science of Weights (Scientia de ponderibus): Treatises Ascribed to Euclid, Archimedes, Thabit ibn Qurra, Jordanus de Nemore, and Blasius of Parma.
Edited by Ernest A. Moody and Marshall Clagett.

2

Thomas of Bradwardine: His "Tractatus de proportionibus." Its Significance for the Development of Mathematical Physics.
Edited and translated by H. Lamar Crosby, Jr.

3

William Heytesbury: Medieval Logic and the Rise of Mathematical Physics.
By Curtis Wilson.

4

The Science of Mechanics in the Middle Ages.
By Marshall Clagett.

5

Galileo Galilei: On Motion *and* On Mechanics.
Translated by I. E. Drabkin and Stillman Drake.

On Motion and *On Mechanics*

Galileo Galilei
ON MOTION *and*
ON MECHANICS

Comprising *De Motu* (*ca.* 1590)

Translated with Introduction and

Notes by I. E. DRABKIN

and *Le Meccaniche* (*ca.* 1600)

Translated with Introduction and

Notes by STILLMAN DRAKE

The University of Wisconsin Press

MADISON, 1960

Published by

THE UNIVERSITY OF WISCONSIN PRESS

430 Sterling Court, Madison 6, Wisconsin

Printed in the United States of America

by the William Byrd Press, Inc., Richmond, Virginia

Library of Congress Catalog Card Number 60–5658

Foreword

It was during the holding of the Institute of the History of Science at Madison in September, 1957 that I first discussed with Mr. Drake the possibility of adding a translation of Galileo's *Le Meccaniche* to the medieval texts and translations being published by the University of Wisconsin. It seemed desirable that historians of science should have this important earlier work of Galileo in English to compare with ancient and medieval material for the purpose of understanding Galileo's development. Later Mr. Drake induced Mr. Drabkin to include a translation of another of the earlier works of Galileo, his *De Motu*. The appearance of the translations of these two works together makes available to a wider public Galileo's first efforts in mechanics. During the preparation of this volume there was some discussion of the question of whether the Italian and Latin texts of these works should be published along with the translations. In spite of the obvious advantages of having text and translations together, it was felt that the masterful Favaro edition was readily enough available to make the republication of the texts unnecessary.

In view of the fact that Galileo occupies a crucial position in the development of early modern mechanics, it may seem strange to the reader that two of his works should be published as a volume in a series of Publications in Medieval Science. Still when the reader compares these works of Galileo with the treatments of mechanics that stretch back through the Middle Ages to antiquity, it will be evident that there are strong bonds between the Galilean works and their predecessors. This is not to deny Galileo's originality but merely confirms that novelty emerges often in the most ancient dress. Furthermore, it will be apparent in these works that Galileo is taking up problems that had become the focus of mechanical discussions since late antiquity. In the *De Motu* Galileo still treats of natural and forced motions as do his predecessors, and the web of influence is complicated but describable, as Koyré and others have shown. In a reorganization of the text Galileo repeats the view held by Crescas and others that "only downward motion may be natural and all upward motion may be forced." His interest in Archimedes and hydrostatics led him to the view adopted by Benedetti earlier that "the speed of natural motion is proportional to the *difference* between the density of the body and the medium." His treatment of the problem of force on an inclined plane is in many respects the most original part of this treatise and should be compared with the treatment in *Le Meccaniche,* although his discussion of motion on an inclined plane was at this date unsatisfactory. His treatment of projectile motion by impressed force, his mention of the idea of a momentary period of rest between projectile motion and its succeeding natural motion, his embracing of the Hipparchian view of the cause of the acceleration of falling bodies as a gradually diminishing residual impressed force left over from the forced motion—all of these views solidly link this work of Galileo with anti-peripatetic mechanics extending from the time of Philoponus to the Renaissance. In *Le Meccaniche,* the second of the works presented in this volume, Galileo presents a very old subject, the analysis of simple machines, but often in an unusual way. He is justly celebrated in this tract for his use and explication of the principle of virtual velocities regardless of the fact that he had found that principle elsewhere. Mr. Drake in his introduction, of course, stresses the originality of Galileo's treatment, particularly in connection with conservation and inertial principles.

I know that my feeling of gratitude toward the translators for the appearance of these careful translations will be widely shared by students of early mechanics, and all of us anxiously await future translations of Messrs. Drabkin and Drake in the field of Renaissance mechanics.

Marshall Clagett

Institute for Research in the Humanities 1960

Contents

ON MOTION

Translated with Introduction
and Notes by
I. E. Drabkin

Introduction

I

The first volume of the National Edition of the works of Galileo, edited in 1890 by Antonio Favaro, contains on pages 251–419, under the title *De Motu,* the contents of certain manuscripts written in Latin in Galileo's own hand. Some of the material had been published for the first time in 1854 in Volume 11 of Eugenio Albèri's edition of Galileo's works, and the rest by Favaro himself in 1883.[1]

In his monographs and in an Avvertimento (pp. 245–49 of the edition in question) Favaro discusses the history of these manuscripts and problems involved in editing the text. Not having examined the manuscripts independently, I have based my account on his, and I shall limit myself to the briefest summary.

The manuscripts contain two early works, an essay and a dialogue, on various aspects of motion, as well as a series of brief notes on the subject. From the type of doctrine espoused and from other indications these writings seem largely, if not entirely, to have been composed during the time that Galileo taught at the University of Pisa, that is, between 1589 and 1592. But the fact that there was no publication makes precise dating impossible.

The writings may indeed have been originally intended for publication, but they certainly were not put into final form by the author. Repetitions in the essay and the presence of alternative versions are some evidence of incompleteness. The precise place where marginal additions and pages containing new material were meant to be inserted is not always clear; and in the case of the essay, the chapters were left unnumbered. Perhaps the

1. Alcuni scritti inediti di Galileo Galilei . . . *Bullettino di Bibliografia e di Storia delle Scienze Matematiche e Fisiche,* 16 (1883), 26–97, 135–57.

author was never satisfied with the substance of these writings. At any rate, his later discoveries on the subject of motion, beginning around the turn of the century, discoveries which were incorporated in a series of works culminating in the *Discourses and Mathematical Demonstrations Concerning Two New Sciences* (published in 1638), rendered the earlier work largely obsolete. And since whatever was fruitful in the earlier work was developed, over the years, in the newer studies, there was less reason, as time passed, for Galileo himself to publish the earlier material as such.

The manuscripts, however, were preserved. And it was the obvious importance of these writings for the study of the evolution of Galileo's thought that prompted Favaro to publish them in full.

The material (pp. 251–419) included by Favaro under the title *De Motu* consists of the following:

1. A text (pp. 251–340) of what Favaro took to be Galileo's first version of an essay on motion.

2. Two texts containing reworkings of portions of the earlier text.

    a. A reworking (pp. 341–43) of the material of pp. 251–53;

    b. A reworking (pp. 344–66) of the material of pp. 251–53 and of parts of pp. 253–60 and 289–94, with additions and omissions.

3. A dialogue (pp. 367–408) dealing with much of the same material as the essay, from the same viewpoint and often in the same language as the essay.

4. A series of fragmentary thoughts, notes, and memoranda (pp. 409–17) almost all on the subject of motion. (The substance of these notes is in most cases incorporated in the text of the essay itself.) Also a set of topics and propositions (pp. 418–19) that form something like a partial plan for Galileo's early work on the subject of motion.

I have limited myself to presenting a translation of the first of the four items listed above, together with some explanatory notes. Some attention has been paid in the notes and in the Appendix to the other three items. But of these the Dialogue, in particular, warrants more extensive treatment than has been possible in the present volume, and I hope to present a separate translation of it at another time.

A word about the translation and notes. In the translation I have occasionally added words of explanation in square brackets to clarify the meaning. And I have taken the liberty of adding chapter numbers, also in brackets. Galileo divided the work into chapters, but, as we have seen, left these unnumbered. In fact, there is doubt about the ordering of some chapters. But the numbering of the twenty-three chapters will facilitate cross reference. I have also added in the margins the page numbers of Favaro's edition, to facilitate reference to the original Latin text. All references will be to the pages of Favaro's edition unless otherwise specified.

Favaro recorded in his *apparatus criticus* and notes every detail of spelling, verbal lapses, deletions, substitutions, marginalia, etc. I have included only such material as seemed important for an understanding of Galileo's thought. Galileo's marginal additions are, of course, included; but the deleted matter (which can still be read) is only occasionally of sufficient importance to reproduce here. I have tried, where possible, to specify in the notes the precise lines (from the Berlin Academy edition of Aristotle and his commentators) that Galileo had in mind in his references. (Galileo generally refers to Aristotle by book and numbered text or section, as given in the medieval commentaries; references such as *De Caelo* 3.28 are so to be understood.)

I have not dealt with matters of linguistic usage as such. But where the text seems to require change in order to make sense (e.g., at 282.1 and 305.28), I have noted that fact.

Of course, the purpose of publishing a text or translation of the essay *De Motu* is to help historians of science to understand the evolution of Galileo's thought and of physics in general. But the limitations of my own knowledge have led me to confine myself merely to the presentation of Galileo's meaning, and not to attempt these broader historical studies. The comparison of the ideas of the *De Motu* with those of Galileo's predecessors and contemporaries and with those that Galileo himself developed later is obviously of the utmost importance. And studies along these lines have been published, some of which I have listed in Section III, below. But my own purpose has not been to present such a study.

A few generalities, however, may not be out of order. The ancient Greeks and their successors from the thirteenth to the sixteenth centuries had made solid progress in statics, but the theories they had evolved in the fields of dynamics and of motion in general, even when internally consistent, proved in the end to be unsatisfactory. Neither were they based on, nor did they directly lead to, fruitful concepts of inertia, force, velocity, and acceleration, and of the precise relations involved. And though the essay *De Motu* did show some insights that were useful for the ultimate discovery of the principle of inertia, still it failed to achieve the clarification requisite for a fruitful theory of motion.

By contrast, the later work, which culminated in the *Discourses,* embodies certain new approaches that were to prove decisive for the future development of physics.

II

What are the ideas of the essay *De Motu?*

To begin with, Galileo adheres to the Aristotelian doctrine of natural places, that heavy bodies tend to move downwards (i.e., toward the center of the universe which, in this essay, would also be the center of the earth), and that the heavier they are, the nearer to the center will be their natural place, i.e., the place where they will be at rest. And in this connection the terms 'lighter' and 'heavier' are defined (ch. 1) on the basis of weight *per unit volume,* so that all bodies have a characteristic or specific weight.

Thus, if a body is heavier, in this sense, than a fluid medium in which it is situated, it will move downward; but if it is lighter, it will move upward. An attempt is made to account for nature's choice of these directions on the basis of the geometric properties of the sphere (ch. 2 and the reworkings).

In the first version of the essay (e.g., ch. 2), such free motion, both upward and downward, is called 'natural'; but in the reworkings Galileo adopts terminology that gives stronger emphasis to the anti-Aristotelian view that properly only downward motion may be natural and all upward motion must be forced. That is, the essential cause of natural downward motion is internal, viz., the weight of the body, while the presence of the medium is accidental and impedes such motion. But the essential cause of 'free' upward motion is external, being the effect of a heavier medium getting beneath the body and pushing it up (extrusion). (The case of projected bodies is taken up later.)

In any case, it is the relative heaviness or lightness of the body and the medium that brings about the free motion of the body therein and determines its direction (ch. 3).

Galileo's approach is based largely on hydrostatic analogies and on the principle of the balance (ch. 4, 5, 6). We must remember, in this connection, how much the youthful Galileo admired and was influenced by Archimedes' successful treatment of statics and hydrostatics.

And so, in passing to the question of the *speed* of natural motion, Galileo takes these same hydrostatic considerations as his point of departure. The difference between the specific weights (or relative densities) of the body and the medium somehow is thought to represent the downward or upward thrust of the body; Galileo makes the speed of natural motion proportional to this difference (ch. 7, 8). And this difference is analogous to the difference of weights in the scales of a balance not in equilibrium, and, as in the case of the balance, is the cause of motion (ch. 9).

But just what does Galileo mean by *the* speed of a body which, let us say, is falling freely in a medium? Is not the speed changing at every moment? Not in Galileo's view, as we shall see; in that view acceleration is an external accident and does not persist. Perhaps *the* speed, then, is that which is established when acceleration ceases, but this is not made clear. In some contexts the distance traversed in a fixed time, beginning from rest, seems to be taken as the measure of speed. But actually, Galileo is not concerned with speed as such but with the ratio of the speeds of the natural motion of different bodies in the same medium, or of the same body in different media, or of different bodies in different media.

The notion that the speed of natural motion is proportional to the *difference* between the density of the body and of the medium enables Galileo to answer all these questions. Thus (in line with anti-Aristotelian tradition) two bodies of the same material but of different size would have the same speed of natural motion (ch. 8 *in.*). In general, $v_{am}/v_{bn} = (d_a - d_m)/(d_b - d_n)$, where v_{am} is the speed of free fall of body a in fluid medium m; d_a is the density of a, etc. And the answers to the other questions are easily derived (ch. 8).

Hence, also, motion in a void (i.e., in a medium with zero density) is not an impossibility (ch. 10); but it is an impossibility for Aristotle, who makes the speed of natural downward motion inversely proportional to the density of the medium.

Aristotle had made the speed of natural downward motion directly proportional to the *total* weight of the moving body. Now Galileo, too, holds that the speed of natural motion depends on weight, not, however, on total weight, but on the *difference* between the weights of *unit volumes* of the body and of the medium through which motion takes place. This leads to more general questions about weight. Here, again, Galileo proceeds on hydrostatic principles. There is no absolutely light or heavy body (ch. 12). All bodies, even fire, have weight as such, i.e., if weighed in a void, where alone the true relations of weight or density are revealed (ch. 13). And they would all, therefore, move downward in a void; but in a nonvacuous fluid medium the relative densities of the body and the medium are controlling. Hence, for example, air would have no *effective* weight in air and would move neither up nor down (ch. 11). In connection with the problem of the speed of natural motion, Galileo while emphasizing hydrostatic principles, gives only brief and hardly sufficient attention to the effect of viscosity of the medium and the shape of the moving body (266).

The force required to keep a frictionless body from moving down an inclined plane is correctly stated in ch. 14 (300). But the proof erroneously links this force with the still unclarified notion of the speed of free fall. And so Galileo is unable to deal successfully with dynamic problems involving the speed of descent on planes of varying inclinations (301-2).

If motion down an inclined plane is 'natural,' and motion up the plane is always 'forced,' then motion on the horizontal plane would seem to be neither natural nor forced (299–300). Actually the surface of which this is true for Galileo is not a plane but a spherical surface concentric with the center of the universe (301). And, more generally, all circular or spherical motions in which the center of gravity of the moving body neither approaches the center of the universe nor recedes from it partake of this neutral character, being intrinsically neither natural nor forced (ch. 16). (In these discussions there may be some progress toward the inertial concept; but no such general concept is stated in the *De Motu.*)

When a missile is thrown straight upward, it can still move when the projector has lost contact with it, not because of any action of the medium (as the Peripatetics held), but because of the force that has been impressed upon it by the projector (ch. 17). Analogies of heat and sound are adduced in support of this view. Now, from the very beginning, this impressed upward force is gradually used up until it is just equal to the intrinsic weight of the body (ch. 18, 19). At that moment the body is at rest, but only instantaneously, not for any interval of time (ch. 20). As the upward impressed force continues to diminish, the body now moves downward and undergoes acceleration until the impressed force is entirely lost. And the theory applies equally to the case of free fall from rest (320). (The possibility that acceleration, and thus, presumably, also the upward impressed force, may together approach zero as a limit, but never reach it, is considered [ch. 21 *fin.*], but only hypothetically.)

Thus, in Galileo's early view, acceleration comes to an end and the downward speed becomes constant. (But this constant velocity is, in this view, due neither to the increased resistance of the medium as the velocity increases nor to the shape of the body; it would be arrived at even in a void and is not to be confused with 'terminal velocity,' as Galileo in later years conceived it.)

The reason, according to Galileo, that this theory of acceleration is not borne out by observation is that the distances over which observation is possible are too small, in the case of bodies of great density, for the entire opposite impressed force to be used up and for acceleration thus to come to an end (329). Moreover, the persistence of acceleration of freely falling bodies may, in some cases, be an optical illusion (Dialogue version, 406-7).

This theory that acceleration is extrinsic and temporary may help to explain why Galileo often speaks simply of speeds, or ratio of speeds, even where accelerated motion is clearly involved. And his inability to reconcile the phenomena with his theory on the subject may be a reason for his failure to publish the essay. At all events, the problem of acceleration is no nearer solution than it was with the Greeks. Like Hipparchus, Galileo tries to link it with the theory of impressed force. He even considers it a fact that, at the beginning of free fall, lighter bodies fall more swiftly than heavier, and attempts to produce an explanation based on the theory of impressed force (ch. 22)!

Years after the composition of the *De Motu*, when he had correctly formulated the basic laws of freely falling bodies, Galileo was able to show that the trajectory of a missile is a parabola, and, under given conditions, to measure the range, elevation, etc., for various angles of elevation. But in our essay he still takes the initial part of the trajectory to be a straight line, and he grapples with the illusory problem of relating the length of that straight line to the angle of elevation for a constant force of projection (ch. 23). It is with this discussion that the essay ends.

III

Some of the ideas of the *De Motu* are found in antiquity, others in the Middle Ages and among Galileo's immediate predecessors in Italy. One might ask which authors Galileo knew directly at the time of the composition of the essay, which indirectly, and what his own contribution was. Though I have attempted no systematic treatment of these questions, there is some discussion of details in the notes. I add here a few general remarks.

The subjects discussed in the essay are largely the subjects that had long been under discussion in academic circles. In view of Galileo's early training, this could hardly be otherwise. But while the solutions to individual problems are not, in general, original discoveries, the work as a whole gives a distinct impression of originality. This is due to the underlying unity of conception, the skillful linking of ideas, the constant recourse to mathematics, and the lucidity of the reasoning and the style.

Without attempting to give anything like a comprehensive bibliography, I may mention some works useful for an understanding of the historical background of the *De Motu*.

Two recent works, E. A. Moody and M. Clagett, *The Medieval Science of Weights* (Madison, 1952), and M. Clagett, *The Science of Mechanics in the Middle Ages* (Madison, 1959), give a large number of original documents (with translation and commentary), mainly from the thirteenth to the sixteenth centuries, bearing on most of the questions that Galileo treats. These books also contain very full and useful bibliographical lists. In these lists the works of Pierre Duhem and Annaliese Maier are especially important.

In order to understand the background of Galileo's essay one must study the development of statics from the Greeks down to the sixteenth century, and, in particular, the work of Jordanus Nemorarius, as well as the history of the criticism of Aristotle's theory of projectile motion and of his theory of the motion of freely falling bodies. Occupying a central position in these latter areas are the theories of impressed force and impetus, as they developed from Hipparchus to the sixteenth century. A summary of the history of these theories is given in Chapter 8 of the work of Clagett on medieval mechanics cited above. And Chapter 9 of the same work deals with the other crucial question—the motion of freely falling bodies.

Two recent works of René Dugas, *Histoire de la Mécanique* (Neuchâtel, 1950), and *La Mécanique au XVII⁰ siècle* (Neuchâtel, 1954), will also be found useful.

Of Galileo's many sixteenth-century Italian predecessors in these fields of study, Francesco Buonamici, who taught at Pisa while Galileo was a student there,[2] and Giovanni Battista Bene-

---

2. Buonamici taught at Pisa for over forty years until his death in 1603. His lectures were, in Favaro's opinion, a chief source of the notes that date from

detti have a special importance for our purpose. They are both supporters of the anti-Aristotelian position at many points, and in the works of one or both of them can be found many of the very ideas that Galileo sets forth in the *De Motu,* e.g., on antiperistasis and the motion of projectiles, on motion in the void, on the factors governing the speed of free fall, etc. Moreover, the details of treatment are, in some cases, remarkably similar. An excellent summary of their works, insofar as they touch the issues of Galileo's essay, is to be found in A. Koyré, *Études Galiléennes,* Part I (Paris, 1939). Koyré gives copious quotations (with translations) from the writings of Buonamici and Benedetti. Benedetti is the subject of two important monographs which also bear on the question of his possible influence on Galileo—G. Vailati, "Speculazioni di Giovanni Benedetti sul moto dei gravi," *Atti della R. Accademia delle scienze di Torino,* 33 (1898), 359–83 (reprinted in G. Vailati, *Scritti,* 161–78 [Leipzig, 1911]); and G. Bordiga, "Giovanni Battista Benedetti filosofo e matematico veneziano del secolo XVI," *Atti del R. Instituto Veneto di Scienze, Lettere, ed Arti,* 85 (1925–26), 585–754.

On the *De Motu* itself not much has been written. Koyré in Part I of his *Études Galiléennes* quotes and translates many basic passages, seeking to show what elements were original and investigating the relation of the early to the later work of Galileo, in particular, to the development of the inertial concept. Raffaele Giacomelli's *Galileo Galilei giovane e il suo "De Motu"* (Pisa, 1949) is devoted to an account of Galileo's early studies and to an analysis of the essay and dialogue *De Motu,* with translations of numerous passages. There are also translations of some passages in Lane Cooper, *Aristotle, Galileo and the Tower of Pisa* (Ithaca, 1935). An analysis of the philosophical tradition behind the ideas of the *De Motu* is given by E. A. Moody in "Galileo and Avempace: The Dynamics of the Leaning Tower Experiment," *Journal of the History of Ideas,* 12 (1951), 163–93, 375–422. Moody sharply differentiates the development of the theory of (a self-expending) impressed force from the so-called 'impetus' theory, and investigates the source of Galileo's knowledge of the former, the theory espoused in the *De Motu.*

In presenting my translation of Galileo's essay *On Motion* I wish to acknowledge with deep gratitude my indebtedness to

---

Galileo's student days, the so-called *Juvenilia;* and a copy of the 1591 edition of Buonamici's *De Motu libri X* was owned by Galileo (so Favaro, Ed. Naz., I, 12).

Mr. Stillman Drake and Professor Edward Rosen who read the manuscript critically and gave me the benefit of their vast knowledge and experience in this field of study, and to my wife, Miriam, who worked alongside me in preparing the manuscript and in seeing it through the press.

I. E. Drabkin

The City College, New York
December, 1959

[Chapter 1]

We are going to explain later on that all natural motion, whether upward or downward,[1] is the result of the essential heaviness[2] or lightness of the moving body. We have therefore thought it logical first to discuss on what basis we are to say that one thing is lighter or heavier than another thing, or is equally heavy. And it is necessary to settle this, for it often happens that what is lighter is called heavier, and conversely. Thus, we sometimes say that a large piece of wood is heavier than a small piece of lead, though lead, as such, is heavier than wood. And we say that a large piece of lead is heavier than a small piece of lead, though lead is not heavier than lead.

Therefore, to avoid pitfalls of this kind, we define as equally heavy two substances which, when they are equal in size [i.e., in volume], are also equal in weight. Thus, if we take two pieces of lead which are equal in volume and equal also in weight, we shall have to say that they are equally heavy.[3] And clearly, therefore, we must not say that wood and lead are equally heavy. For a piece of wood which weighs the same as a piece of lead will far exceed the piece of lead in volume.

1. In the later reworking (361–64: see Appendix I), Galileo ascribes the term "natural" only to the free downward motion of a body in a lighter medium, holding that all upward motion is forced.
2. This "essential heaviness" (*propria gravitas*) is defined in what follows and is, in a broad sense, the equivalent of specific gravity or relative density. Throughout the treatise "weight" or "heaviness" has this sense of relative density, unless otherwise noted.
3. In a reworking (see Appendix I), Galileo uses the more significant example (348.1) that silver and steel are equally heavy if equal volumes of them have the same weight.

Again, one substance should be called heavier than a second substance, if a piece of the first, equal in volume to a piece of the second, is found to weigh more than the second. For example, if we take a piece of lead and a piece of wood equal in volume to each other, and the piece of lead is heavier than the piece of wood, then we shall certainly be right in asserting that lead is heavier than wood. Therefore, if we find a piece of wood equal in weight to a piece of lead, surely we must not con-
252   clude that wood and lead are equally heavy. For we shall find that in such a case the volume of the lead is far exceeded by the volume of the wood.

And, finally, we must define, in converse fashion, that which is lighter.[4] That is, one substance is to be considered lighter than a second substance, if a portion of the first, equal in volume to a portion of the second, is found to weigh less than the second. Thus, if we take two pieces, one of wood and one of lead, equal to each other in volume, and the piece of wood weighs less than the piece of lead, then we shall properly conclude that wood is lighter than lead.

4. From what precedes, this term is to be understood in the sense of "less heavy." Galileo makes clearer in the reworkings (see Appendix I) that all bodies have weight and all tend to move naturally toward the center of the universe, so that all motion away from the center (i.e., upward) is "forced."

[Chapter 2]

That heavy substances are by nature located in a lower place, and light substances in a higher place, and why.

Since things that move naturally move to their proper places, and since the things that move are either heavy or light, we must consider which are the places of the heavy, and which the places of the light, and why. Now every day we observe with our senses that the places of the heavy are those which are closer to the center of the universe, and the places of the light those which are farther distant. Therefore we have no reason to doubt that such places have been determined for them by nature. On the other hand, there might be some doubt as to why a prudent nature observed this arrangement in distributing the places, rather than the opposite arrangement.

Now, so far as I have read, no other reason for the existing arrangement is adduced by the philosophers than that everything must be disposed in some arrangement, and that it has pleased

Providence on high to employ this arrangement. It seems that Aristotle also adduces this reason (*Physics* 8.32),[1] when, in investigating why heavy and light bodies move to their proper places, he suggests that the reason is that they have a natural tendency to move in some direction, that is, the light upward, and the heavy downward.[2] Yet, if we look at the matter more carefully, surely we shall not have to conclude that nature was under no necessity in this arrangement, and obtained no advantage from it, and that she somehow operated solely according to whim and chance.

Since I believed that it was impossible to entertain such a view about provident nature, I anxiously sought from time to time to think of some cause, if not necessary, at least reasonable and useful. And, in truth, I have found that nature chose the existing arrangement with complete justice and with consummate wisdom. For if it is true, as ancient philosophers[3] believed, that there is a single kind of matter in all bodies, and those bodies are heavier which enclose more particles of that matter in a narrower space

253   (as those same philosophers asserted, for which they were perhaps wrongly criticized by Aristotle in *De Caelo,* Book 4),[4] then surely it was logical that bodies containing more matter in a narrower space should also occupy narrower places, such as are those that are nearer the center.

If, for example, we suppose that nature, at the time of the construction of the universe, divided all the common matter of the elements into four equal[5] parts, and then assigned to the form of the earth its own matter [i.e., earth], and likewise to the form of air *its* own matter [i.e., air], and that the form of the earth caused its matter to be compressed in a very narrow space, while the form of the air permitted the placing of its matter in a very ample space, would it not be reasonable for nature to assign a large space to air, and a smaller space to earth? But in a sphere the spaces become narrower as we approach the center, and larger as we recede from the center.

It was therefore with both prudence and justice that nature

---

1. 255b15–17. (Cf. the statement in the dialogue version 374.18–24; see p. 125, below.)

2. Marginal addition: "Ptolemy, at the beginning of ch. 7 of Book I of the *Syntaxis* says that it is vain to inquire *why* heavy bodies are carried toward the center, after he had demonstrated that the earth toward which they are carried is in the center" (F).

3. E.g., monists and atomists.

4. 308b–309b.

5. This word was omitted from Galileo's later versions (at 343.12 and 345.22).

determined as the place of earth one that was too narrow for the
other elements, i.e., near the center; and for the other elements
places more spacious in proportion as the matter of each of those
elements was rarer. I should not, however, say[6] that the amount
of aqueous matter is precisely as great as that of terrestrial matter
and, therefore, that water, since it is rarer than earth, occupies
larger spaces. I merely say that if we consider a portion of water
equal in weight to a portion of earth, and if, therefore, the quantity of aqueous matter [under consideration] is equal to that of
terrestrial matter, then surely that portion of earth will occupy a
smaller space than the water, and hence should properly be located in a narrower space, i.e., nearer the center.[7] And if we similarly consider the other elements, we shall find a certain harmony, not to say necessity, in this disposition of the heavy and
the light.

6. A later version (345.31) adds parenthetically "as Aristotle believed."
7. Marginal addition: "The form of air filled a very large space with the same
amount of matter as the form of the earth contained in a narrow place. Therefore
nature must have assigned to air a larger space than to earth" (F).

[Chapter 3]

That natural motion is caused by heaviness or lightness.

In the previous chapter we asserted, and assumed it as well
known, that nature has so arranged it that heavier bodies remain
at rest under lighter. We must, therefore, now note that bodies
which move downward move because of their heaviness, while
those that move upward move because of their lightness.[1] For,
since heavy bodies have, by reason of their heaviness, the property
of remaining at rest under lighter bodies—inasmuch as they are
heavy, they have been placed by nature under the lighter—they
will also have the property, imposed by nature, that, when they
are situated above lighter bodies, they will move down below
these lighter bodies, lest the lighter remain at rest under the
heavier, contrary to the arrangement of nature. And,
254   in the same way, light bodies will move upward by
their lightness, whenever they are under heavier
bodies. For if they have, by reason of their lightness, the property
of remaining at rest above heavier bodies, they will also, by that
same lightness, have the property of *not* remaining at rest below
heavier bodies, unless they are constrained.

Now it is clear from this that, in the case of motion, we must

1. I.e., because of their "lesser heaviness," free upward motion coming about
when a body is immersed in a heavier medium.

consider not merely the lightness or heaviness of the moving body, but also the heaviness or lightness of the medium through which the motion takes place. For if water were not lighter than stone, a stone would not sink in water. But a difficulty might arise at this point, as to why a stone cast into the sea moves downward naturally, despite the fact that the [sum total of] water of the sea is far heavier than the stone that was thrown. We must therefore recall what we pointed out in chapter [1], viz., that the stone is, in fact, heavier than the water of the sea, if we take a quantity of water equal in volume to that of the stone; and so the stone, being heavier than the water, will move downward in the water.

But again a difficulty will arise as to just why we must consider a quantity of water equal in volume to the volume of the stone, rather than of the whole sea. In order to remove this difficulty, I have decided to adduce some proofs, on which not only the solution of this difficulty, but the whole discussion will depend. Though, to be sure, there are many media through which motions take place, e.g., fire, air, water, etc., and in all of them the same principle applies, we shall assume that water is the medium in which the motion is to take place. And first we shall prove that bodies equally heavy with the water itself, if let down into the water, are completely submerged, but then move neither downward nor upward. Secondly, we shall show that bodies lighter than water not only do not sink in the water, but are not even completely submerged. Thirdly, we shall prove that bodies heavier than water necessarily move downward.

[Chapter 4]

First Demonstration,
in which it is proved that bodies of the same heaviness as the medium move neither upward nor downward.

Coming now to the proofs, let us first consider a body of the same heaviness as water, i.e., one whose weight is equal to the weight of a quantity of water equal in volume to the volume of the given body. Let the body be *ef*. It must then be proved that body *ef*, if let down into the water, is completely submerged, and then moves neither upward nor downward. Let *abcd* be the position of the water,[1] before the body is let down into it. And suppose that body *ef*, after being

255

1. In the dialogue version the diagrams indicate that the surface of the water is taken as spherical. The proofs are essentially the same.

let down into the water, is not completely submerged, if that is possible, but that some part of it, say *e,* protrudes, only part *f* being submerged. While part *f* of the body is being submerged, the level of the water is necessarily raised. Thus, suppose surface *ao* of the water is raised to surface *st.* Clearly, the volume of water *so* is exactly equal to the volume of *f,* the submerged part of the body. For it is necessary that the space into which the body enters be vacated by the water, and that a volume of water be removed equal to the volume of that portion of the body that is submerged. Therefore the volume of water *so* is equal to the volume of the submerged part *f* of the body. Hence also the weight of *f* will equal the weight of water *so.*

Now the water *so* strives by its weight to return downwards to its original position, but cannot achieve this unless solid *ef* is first lifted out of the water, i.e., raised by the action of the water. And the solid resists such raising with all the weight that it has; moreover, both the solid body and the water are assumed to be at rest in this position. Therefore the weight of water *so,* by which the water strives to raise the solid upward, must necessarily be equal to the weight with which the solid resists and presses downward. (For if the weight of water *so* were greater than the weight of solid *ef, ef* would be raised and forced out of the water; if, on the other hand, the weight of solid *ef* were greater, the water level would be raised. But everything is assumed to be at rest in this position.) Hence the weight of water *so* is equal to the weight of the whole magnitude *ef.* But that is impossible, for the weight of *so* is equal to that of part *f.* It is clear, therefore, that no part of the solid magnitude *ef* will protrude [above the water level], but that the whole will be submerged.

This is the complete demonstration which I have set forth in fuller detail so that those who come upon it for the first time may be able to understand it more easily. But it might be better explained more briefly, so that the entire heart of the proof would be as follows. We must prove that magnitude *ef,* which is assumed to be of the same weight as water, is completely submerged. Suppose, then, if it is *not* completely submerged, that some part of it protrudes. Let *e* be the part protruding, and let the water level be raised to the surface *st;* and, if possible, let the water and the body both be at rest in this position. Then, since magnitude *ef* presses by its weight and tends to raise water *so,* and water *so* by its weight resists being further raised, it must follow that the weight of *ef* pressing down is exactly equal to the weight of water *so* which resists.

256

For since they are assumed to be at rest in this position, neither will the pressure be greater than the resistance, nor the resistance greater than the pressure. Hence the weight of water *so* is equal to the weight of magnitude *ef*. But this is impossible. For, since the volume of the whole body *ef* is greater than the volume of the water *so*, the weight of body *ef* will also be greater than that of the water *so*. It is therefore clear that bodies of the same heaviness as water will be completely submerged in water.

And I say further that they will move neither upward nor downward, but will remain at rest wherever they are placed. For there is no reason why they should move downward or upward. Since they are assumed to be of the same heaviness as water, to say that they sink in water would be the same as saying that water, when placed in water, sinks underneath this water; and then that the water which rises above the first-mentioned water again moves downward, and that the water thus continues to move alternately downward and upward forever. This is impossible.

[Chapter 5]

Second Demonstration,
in which it is proved that bodies lighter than water
cannot be completely submerged.

Now since the demonstration in the previous chapter had to do with a state of rest,[1] we must now consider a case which involves motion upward. I say, then, that bodies lighter than water, when let down into water, are not completely submerged, but that some portion protrudes. Let the first level of the water, before the body is let down, be along surface *ef;* and suppose that body *a,* lighter than water, is let down into the water, and, if possible, is completely submerged, and the water level raised to surface *cd.* And suppose, if it is possible, that both the water and the body remain at rest in this position. Now the weight with which the body exerts pressure and tends to raise water *cf* will be equal to the weight with which water *cf* exerts pressure to raise body *a.* But the volume of water *cf* is equal to that of body *a.* There are therefore two magnitudes, one the body *a,* the other the water *cf;* and the weight of *a* is equal to that of *cf,* and also the volume of *a* is equal to the volume of the water *cf.* Therefore body *a* is of the same heaviness as the water. But this is impos-

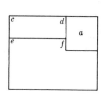

---

1. In the sense that the bodies in question, when placed anywhere in the water, provided they were completely submerged, remained at rest.

sible: for the body was assumed to be lighter than water. Therefore body *a* will not remain completely submerged under the
water. It will therefore of necessity move upward.

257   It is clear, then, why and how motion upward results from lightness. And, from what has been said in
this and in the previous chapter, it can easily be understood that
bodies heavier than water are completely submerged and must
keep moving downward. That they are completely submerged is
a necessary conclusion. For if they were not completely submerged, they would be lighter than water, and this would be
contrary to our assumption. For it follows from the converse of
the proposition just proved that bodies which are not completely
submerged are lighter than water. Moreover, these bodies [i.e.,
those heavier than water] must continue to move downward. For
if they did not move downward, they would either be at rest or
move upward. But they could not be at rest: for it was proved in
the preceding chapter that bodies having the same heaviness as
water remain at rest and move neither upward nor downward.[2]
And it has just been shown that bodies lighter than water move
upward. Therefore, from all these considerations, since bodies
which move downwards must be heavier than the medium
through which they move, it is clear that heavy bodies move
downward by reason of their weight. And it is clear that, in the
case of the stone thrown into the sea, we must reckon not with
all the water of the sea, but only with that small part which is
removed from the place into which the stone enters.

But the points set forth in these last two chapters cannot very
well be further elucidated mathematically; they require rather
a physical explanation. For this reason I propose, in the next
chapter, to reduce the matter to a consideration of the balance,
and to explain the analogy that holds between bodies that move
naturally and the weights of the balance. My aim is a richer comprehension of the matters under discussion, and a more precise
understanding on the part of my readers.

2. The truth of the converse is assumed, and could, in any case, be proved
without difficulty. So also three sentences earlier.

Chapter [6]

In which is explained the analogy between bodies moving naturally and the weights of a balance.

We shall first consider what happens in the case of the balance,
so that we may then show that all these things also happen in the

case of bodies moving naturally. Let line *ab,* then, represent a
balance, whose center, over which motion may take place, is the
point *c* bisecting line *ab.* And let two weights, *e* and *o,* be sus-

pended from points *a* and *b.* Now in the case of weight *e* there
are three possibilities: it may either be at rest, or move upward,
or move downward. Thus if weight *e* is heavier than
weight *o,* then *e* will move downward. But if *e* is less
heavy, it will, of course, move upward, and not because it does not have weight, but because the weight of *o* is
greater. From this it is clear that, in the case of the balance, motion upward as well as motion downward takes place because of
weight, but in a different way. For motion upward will occur for
e on account of the weight of *o,* but motion downward on account of its own weight. But if the weight of *e* is equal to that
of *o,* then *e* will move neither upward nor downward. For *e* will
not move downward unless weight *o,* which tends to raise it, is
less heavy; nor will *e* move upward unless weight *o,* by which it
must be raised, is heavier.

258

Having examined the case of the balance, we return to naturally moving bodies. We can assert this general proposition:
that the heavier cannot be raised by the less heavy. On this assumption it is easy to understand why solids lighter than water
are not completely submerged.

If, for example, we let a piece of wood down into water, then,
if the wood is to be submerged, water must necessarily leave the
place into which the wood enters, and this water must be raised,
that is, must be moved in a direction away from the center of the
universe. If, then, the water which has to be raised is heavier than
the wood, it surely will not be able to be raised by the wood. But
if the whole piece of wood is submerged, then from the place
into which the wood enters a volume of water must be removed
equal to the volume of the whole piece of wood. But a volume of
water equal to the volume of the wood is heavier than the wood
(for it is assumed that the wood is lighter than water). It will
therefore not be possible for the wood to be completely submerged. And this is in agreement with what was said in the case
of the balance, namely, that a smaller weight cannot raise a larger.

But if the wood were of the same heaviness as the water, that
is, if the water which is raised by the complete submerging of the
wood is not heavier than but only just as heavy as the wood, the

wood will of course then be completely submerged, since it does not meet [sufficient][1] resistance from the lifting action of the water. But once it is entirely submerged it does not continue to move either upward or downward. And this corresponds an-alogically to what was said, in the case of the balance, about equal weights neither of which moves upward or downward.

But if, on the other hand, the wood is heavier than that part of the water which tends to be lifted by the wood, that is to say, if the wood is heavier than a volume of water equal to the vol-ume of the wood (for, as has often been said, the volume of water that is lifted by the submerged wood is equal to the volume of the wood), then surely the wood will continue to move down-ward. And this corresponds analogically to what was said in the case of the balance—namely, that one weight moves down and sends the other one up when it is heavier than that other.

259

Besides, in the case of bodies moving naturally, as in the weights in a balance, the cause of all motions, up as well as down, can be referred to weight alone. For when something moves up,[2] it is at that time being raised by the weight of the medium. Thus, if a piece of wood lighter than water is forcibly held under water, then, since the submerged wood displaces a volume of water equal to its own volume, and since a volume of water equal to the volume of the wood is heavier than the piece of wood, doubt-less the wood will be lifted by the weight of that water and will be impelled upward. Thus upward motion will occur because of the heaviness of the medium and the [relative] lightness of the moving body; and downward motion because of the heaviness of the moving body and the [relative] lightness of the medium.

And from this one can easily understand (contrary to Aristotle *De Caelo* 1.89)[3] that what moves moves, as it were, by force[4] and

---

1. I.e., sufficient to keep it from being entirely submerged.

2. I.e., in so-called "natural" motion.

3. 277b1–8.

4. I.e., that so-called "natural" motion is a kind of forced motion. In the reworking of this section (see Appendix I), Galileo specifically classes all upward motion as "forced" motion. But he continues to consider free downward motion as "natural," since it would take place independently of a medium, i.e., in a void. Cf. the memorandum (413.27): "Downward motion is far more natural than upward. For upward motion depends entirely on the heaviness of the me-dium, which confers on the moving body an accidental lightness; but downward motion is caused by the intrinsic heaviness of the moving body. In the absence of a medium everything will move downward. Upward motion is caused by the extruding action of a heavy medium. Just as, in the case of a balance, the lighter weight is forcibly moved upward by the heavier, so the moving body is forcibly pushed upward by the heavier medium."

by the extruding action of the medium. For when the wood is forcibly submerged, the water violently thrusts it out when, with downward motion, it moves toward its own proper place and is unwilling to permit that which is lighter than itself to remain at rest under it. In the same way, the stone is thrust from its position and impelled downward because it is heavier than the medium. It is therefore clear that this kind of motion may be called "forced," although commonly the upward motion of wood in water and the downward motion of stone in water are called "natural." And Aristotle's argument is invalid when he says: "If the motion were forced, it would lose speed at the end and not gain it, as it does."[5] For forced motion loses speed only when the moving body leaves the hand of the mover, not while it is still in contact with the mover.

It is therefore clear that the motion of bodies moving naturally can be suitably reduced to the motion of weights in a balance. That is, the body moving naturally plays the role of one weight in the balance, and a volume of the medium equal to the volume of the moving body represents the other weight in the balance. So that, if a volume of the medium equal to the volume of the moving body is heavier than the moving body, and the moving body lighter, then the latter, being the lighter weight, will move up. But if the moving body is heavier than the same volume of the medium, then, being the heavier weight, it will move down. And if, finally, the said volume of the medium has a weight equal to that of the moving body, the latter will move neither up nor down, just as the weights in the balance, when they are equal to each other, neither fall nor rise.

260   And since the comparison of bodies in natural motion and weights on a balance is a very appropriate one, we shall demonstrate this parallelism throughout the whole ensuing discussion of natural motion. Surely this will contribute not a little to the understanding of the matter.

5. 277b6–8.

Chapter [7]

The cause of speed and slowness of natural motion.

Since it has been quite fully explained above that natural motions are caused by heaviness and lightness, we must now consider how the greater or lesser speed of such motion comes about. In order to be able to accomplish this more easily, we must make the following distinction, viz., that inequalities in the slowness and speed of motion occur in two ways: either the same body moves in different media, or else there are different bodies moving in the same medium.[1] We shall show presently that in both these cases of motion the slowness and speed depend on the same cause, namely, the greater or lesser weight of the media and of the moving bodies.[2] But first we shall show that the cause given by Aristotle to account for this effect is insufficient.

Aristotle wrote (*Physics* 4.71)[3] that the same body moves more swiftly in a rarer than in a denser medium, and that therefore the cause of slowness of motion is the density of the medium, and the cause of speed its rareness. And he asserted this on the basis of no other reason than experience, viz., that we see a moving body move more swiftly in air than in water.

But it will be easy to prove that this reason is not sufficient. For if the speed of motion depends on the rareness of the
261   medium, the same body will always move more swiftly through rarer media. But this is erroneous. For there are many moving bodies that move more swiftly with natural motion in denser media than they do in rarer ones, e.g., more swiftly in water than in air. If, for example, we take a very thin inflated bladder, it will descend slowly with natural motion in air. But if we release it[4] in deep water, it will fly up very fast, again with natural motion.[5] At this point I know that someone may reply that the bladder moves in air and is swiftly[6] carried down, but in water not only does it not fall faster, it does not fall at all. I would say in answer that the bladder moves up very swiftly in the water, but then does not continue moving in the air. But, not to prolong the argument, I say that in the rarer media not every motion, but only downward motion, is swifter; and upward motion is swifter in denser media. And this is reasonable. For in a place where a downward motion takes place with difficulty, an upward motion necessarily takes place with ease. Clearly, then, the statement of Aristotle that slowness of natural motion is due to the density of the medium is inadequate.

Therefore, dismissing his opinion, so that we may adduce the

1. The third case, different bodies in different media, is reducible to the other two. Cf. 273, below.
2. Marginal note: "Note at this point that we are speaking of the first and formal cause, not of an accidental and external cause, such as the shape of the moving body or the thickness of the medium" (F).
3. 215a31–b12.
4. *Dimittatur* (for *demittatur* 261.6) would be expected.
5. For the purpose of his rather superficial argument, Galileo must speak of free upward motion as "natural."
6. Galileo may have meant to write *tarde* (261.8).

true cause of slowness and speed of motion, we must point out that speed cannot be separated from motion. For whoever asserts motion necessarily asserts speed; and slowness is nothing but lesser speed. Speed therefore proceeds from the same [cause] from which motion proceeds. And since motion proceeds from heaviness and lightness, speed or slowness must necessarily proceed from the same source. That is, from the greater heaviness of the moving body there results a greater speed of the motion, namely, downward motion, which comes about from the heaviness of that body; and from a lesser heaviness [of the body], a slowness of that same motion. On the other hand, from a greater lightness of the moving body will result a greater speed in that motion which comes about from the lightness of the body, namely, upward motion.

Thus it is clear that a difference in the speed and slowness of motion occurs in the case of different bodies moving in the same medium. For if the motion is downward, the heavier substance will move more swiftly than the lighter; and if the motion is upward, that which is lighter will move more swiftly. But whether two bodies moving in the same medium maintain the same ratio between the speed of their motions as there is between their weights, as Aristotle believed,[7] will be considered below.

And in the case of the speed and slowness of the same body moving in different media, the situation is similar. 262   The body moves downward more swiftly in that medium in which it is heavier, than in another in which it is less heavy; and it moves upward more swiftly in that medium in which it is lighter, than in another in which it is less light. Hence it is clear that if we find in what media a given body is heavier, we shall have found media in which it will fall more swiftly. And if, furthermore, we can show how much heavier that same body is in this medium than in that, we shall have shown how much more swiftly it will move downward in this medium than in that. Conversely, in considering lightness, when we find a medium in which a given body will be lighter, we shall have found a medium in which it will rise more swiftly; and if we find how much lighter the given body is in this medium than in that, we shall also have found how much more swiftly the body will rise in this medium than in that.

But in order that all this may be more precisely grasped in any particular case of motion, we shall first speak of the motions of

7. E.g., *Physics* 216a13–16.

different bodies in the same medium, and show what ratio there is between these motions, with respect to slowness and speed. We shall then consider motions of the same body moving in different media, and show, likewise, what ratio there is between the motions.

Chapter [8]

In which it is shown that different bodies moving in the same medium maintain a ratio [of their speeds] different from that attributed to them by Aristotle.

In order to deal more easily with the matters under investigation, we must understand, in the first place, that a difference between two such bodies can arise in two ways. They may be of the same material, e.g., both lead, or both iron, and differ in size [i.e., volume]; or else they may be of different materials, e.g., one iron, the other wood, and differ either in size and weight, or in weight but not size, or in size but not weight.

263   Of those [naturally] moving bodies which are of the same material, Aristotle said that the larger moves more swiftly. This is found in *De Caelo* 4.26,[1] where he wrote that any body of fire moves upward, and that body which is larger moves faster; also that any body of earth moves downward, and, similarly, that that body which is larger moves faster. Aristotle also wrote (*De Caelo* 3.26):[2] "Suppose a heavy body *b* moves on line *ce,* which is divided at point *d*. If, then, body *b* is divided in the same ratio as line *ce* is divided by *d,* clearly a part of *b* will move over line *cd* in the same time as the whole of *b* moves over the whole line *ce.*" From this it is obvious that Aristotle holds that, in the case of bodies of the same material, the ratio of the speeds of their [natural] motion is equal to the ratio of the sizes of the bodies. And he puts this most clearly when he says (*De Caelo* 4.16)[3] that a large piece of gold moves more swiftly than a small piece.

But how ridiculous this view is, is clearer than daylight. For who will ever believe that if, for example, two lead balls, one a hundred times as large as the other, are let fall from the sphere of the moon,[4] and if the larger comes down to the earth in one hour,

---

1. 311a19–22, b6–13.
2. 301a27–32.
3. 309b14.
4. I.e., the sphere on whose surface is described the moon's orbit around the earth. The sublunary region is, in the Peripatetic system, the region in which

the smaller will require one hundred hours for its motion? Or that, if two stones, one twice the size of the other, are thrown from the top of a high tower at the same moment, the larger reaches the ground when the smaller is only halfway down from the top of the tower?[5] Or, again, if a very large piece of wood and a small piece of the same wood, the large piece being a hundred times the size of the small one, begin to rise from the bottom of the sea at the same time, who would ever say that the large piece would rise to the surface of the water a hundred times more swiftly?

But, to employ reasoning at all times rather than examples (for what we seek are the causes of effects, and these causes are not given to us by experience), we shall set forth our own view, and its confirmation will mean the collapse of Aristotle's view. We say, then, that bodies of the same kind (and let "bodies of the same kind" be defined as those that are made of the same material, e.g., lead, wood, etc.), though they may differ in size, still move with the same speed, and a larger stone does not fall more swiftly than a smaller. Those who are surprised by this conclusion will also be surprised by the fact that a very large piece of wood can float on water, no less than a small piece. For the reasoning is the same.

264

Thus, if we imagine that the water on which a large piece of wood and a small piece of the same wood are afloat, is gradually made successively lighter, so that finally the water becomes lighter than the wood, and both pieces slowly begin to sink, who could ever say that the large piece would sink first or more swiftly than the small piece? For, though the large piece of wood is heavier than the small one, we must nevertheless consider the large piece in connection with the large amount of water that tends to be raised by it, and the small piece of wood in connection with the correspondingly small amount of water. And since the volume of water to be raised by the large piece of wood is equal to that of the wood itself, and similarly with the small piece, those two quantities of water, which are raised by the respective pieces of wood, have the same ratio to each other in their weights as do their volumes (for portions of the same substance are to each other in weight as they are in volume; which would have to be

---

rectilinear motion occurs, and so the bodies are conceived as falling from the extremity of that region to the earth.

5. Galilean and pre-Galilean references to experiments of this kind are collected in Lane Cooper, *Aristotle, Galileo, and the Tower of Pisa* (Ithaca, 1935). See also the article of E. A. Moody cited at the end of the Introduction.

proved)[6]—i.e., the same ratio as that of the volumes of the large
and the small piece of wood. Therefore the ratio of the weight of
the large piece of wood to the weight of the water that it tends
to raise is equal to the ratio of the weight of the small piece of
wood to the weight of the water that *it* tends to raise. And the
resistance of the large amount of water will be overcome by the
large piece of wood with the same ease as the resistance of the
small amount of water will be overcome by the small piece of
wood.

Again, if we imagine, for example, a large piece of wax floating
on water, and we mix this wax either with sand or with some
other heavier substance, so that it ultimately becomes heavier than
the water and just barely begins to sink very slowly, who could
ever believe, if we take a small piece of that wax, say one-hundredth part, that it would either not sink at all or would sink a
hundred times more slowly than the whole piece of wax? Surely
no one. And one may make the same experiment with the balance. For if the weights on both sides are equal and very large,
and then some weight, but a small one, is added to one side, the
heavier side will fall, but not any faster than if the weights were
small. Similarly in the case of the water: the large piece of wood
represents one weight in the balance, and the other weight is represented by a volume of water equal to the volume of the wood.
Now if this volume of water is of equal weight with the large
piece of wood, the wood will not sink. But if the wood is made
a little heavier so that it sinks, it will not sink any faster than will
a small piece of the same wood, which at first weighed the same
as an [equally] small volume of water, and then was made a little
bit heavier.

But we may reach this same conclusion by another argument.
Let us first make this assumption: if there are two
265   bodies of which one moves [in natural motion] more
swiftly than the other, a combination of the two
bodies will move more slowly than that part which by itself
moved more swiftly, but the combination will move more swiftly
than that part which by itself moved more slowly.[7] Thus, if we
consider two bodies, e.g., a piece of wax and an inflated bladder,
both moving upward from deep water, but the wax more slowly

6. The material in parentheses is a marginal addition (F). The proof is given
in a reworking of part of the *De Motu* (348–49).

7. The words of this sentence after the colon are underlined in the manuscript.
And there is the following note on them in the margin: "Aristotle makes this
same assumption in his solution of the 24th Mechanical Problem" (F). [Cf.
855b34–36.]

than the bladder, our assumption is that if both are combined, the combination will rise more slowly than the bladder alone, and more swiftly than the wax alone. Indeed it is quite obvious. For who can doubt that the slowness of the wax will be diminished by the speed of the bladder, and, on the other hand, that the speed of the bladder will be retarded by the slowness of the wax, and that some motion will result intermediate between the slowness of the wax and the speed of the bladder?

Similarly, if two bodies move downward [in natural motion], one more slowly than the other, for example, if one is wood and the other an [inflated] bladder, both falling in air, the wood more swiftly than the bladder, our assumption is as follows: if they are combined, the combination will fall more slowly than the wood alone, but more swiftly than the bladder alone. For it is clear that the speed of the wood will be retarded by the slowness of the bladder, and the slowness of the bladder will be accelerated by the speed of the wood; and, as before, some motion will result intermediate between the slowness of the bladder and the speed of the wood.

On the basis of this assumption, I argue as follows in proving that bodies of the same material but of unequal volume move [in natural motion] with the same speed.[8] Suppose there are two bodies of the same material, the larger *a,* and the smaller *b,* and suppose, if it is possible, as asserted by our opponent, that *a* moves [in natural motion] more swiftly than *b.* We have, then, two bodies of which one moves more swiftly. Therefore, according to our assumption, the combination of the two bodies will move more slowly than that part which by itself moved more swiftly than the other. If, then, *a* and *b* are combined, the combination will move more slowly than *a* alone. But the combination of *a* and *b* is larger than *a* is alone. Therefore, contrary to the assertion of our opponents, the larger body will move more slowly than the smaller. But this would be self-contradictory.[9]

| a | b |

8. Marginal note: "And, I pray, let not Themistius laugh, who says (On *Physics* 4.74 [cf. Themistius, *In Aristotelis Physica Paraphrasis,* p. 132.21–26, ed. H. Schenkl]): 'If, for example, the man who casts anchors should be asked why, in the same depth of sea, the ten-pound anchor sinks more swiftly than the three-pound one, will he not answer with a laugh: "Surely here is a question important enough to be referred to Apollo—why the ten-pound anchor is heavier than the three-pound one!"?' " (F).

9. That homogeneous bodies of differing size fall in the same medium with equal speeds had been asserted some years before by G. B. Benedetti (Preface to *De Resolutione omnium Euclidis Problematum* [Venice, 1553]) and by Cardan (*Opus Novum de Proportionibus* V. prop. 110, p. 104 [Basel, 1570]). The proof given by Benedetti in *Diversarum speculationum mathematicarum et physicarum*

266   What clearer proof do we need of the error of Aristotle's opinion? And who, I ask, will not recognize
the truth at once, if he looks at the matter simply and naturally?
For if we suppose that bodies *a* and *b* are equal and are very close
to each other, all will agree that they will move with equal speed.
And if we imagine that they are joined together while moving,
why, I ask, will they double the speed of their motion, as Aristotle
held, or increase their speed at all? Let us then consider it sufficiently corroborated that there is no reason *per se* why bodies of
the same material should move [in natural motion] with unequal
velocities, but every reason why they should move with equal
velocity. Of course, if there were some accidental reason,[10] e.g.,
the shape of the bodies, this will not be considered among causes
per se. Moreover, as we shall show in the proper place,[11] the
shape of the body helps or hinders its motion only to a small
extent.

Still we must not immediately go to extremes, as many do, and
compare, say, a large piece of lead with a very thin plate or even
leaf of the same substance, which would sometimes even float on
water. For since there is a certain cohesiveness of the parts both
of air and of water, and, so to speak, a tenacity and viscosity, this
cannot be overcome by a very small weight. Our conclusion must
therefore be understood to apply to [two] bodies when the weight
and volume of the smaller of them are large enough not to be
impeded by the small viscosity of the medium, e.g., a leaden
sphere of one pound. Moreover, as for those scoffers who, perhaps, believe that they can defend Aristotle, what happens to
them if they have recourse to extremes is that they get into deeper
difficulties, the greater the difference between the bodies which
they take for comparison. For if one of the bodies is a thousand
times as large as the other, surely these people must do some toil-
ing and sweating before they can show that the velocity of one
is a thousand times that of the other.

But, to come to the next point, we must now consider the ratio
[of the speed] of motion of bodies of *different* material moving

---

liber (Turin, 1585), p. 174 (cited by A. Koyré, *Études Galiléennes,* I, 53) has
to do with homogeneous bodies moving in the void, but could apply to any
medium. Though it is widely held (see Introduction, Section III) that Galileo
was here influenced by Benedetti, it should be noted that Benedetti's proof involves the severing of connected weights (cf. Aristotle, *De Caelo* 301), while
Galileo's involves the joining of separate weights. Galileo repeats his argument in
the *Discourses* (E.N., VIII, 107).

10. I.e., for inequality of the velocity of two bodies of the same material.
11. This promise is not fulfilled.

[with natural motion] in the same medium. Though such bodies may differ from each other in three ways—either in size but not in weight, or in weight but not in size, or in both weight and size—we must examine only the case of those that differ in weight but not in size. For the ratios of those that differ in the two other ways can be reduced to this one. Thus in the case of bodies differing in size but not in weight, if from the larger we take a part equal to the smaller, the bodies will then differ in weight, but not in size. And the *whole* of the larger body will, with the smaller body, maintain the same ratio [in the speed of their motions] as will the *part* taken from the larger body. For it has been proved that bodies of the same material, though they differ in size, move with the same velocity.

267

Similarly, in the case of bodies differing both in size and weight, if we take from the larger a part equal [in size] to the smaller, we shall again have two bodies differing in weight, but not in size. And the *part* [of the larger body] will, with the smaller, keep the same ratio [in the speed] of their motions, as will the *whole* of the larger body. For, once again, in the case of bodies of the same material, the part and the whole move with the same speed. It is therefore clear that, if we know the ratio of the speeds of those bodies that differ only in weight, but not in size, we also know the ratios of those that differ in every other way. And so,[12] in order to find this ratio and to show, in opposi-

---

12. The rest of the paragraph is substituted in the margin for the longer passage which we now give in this note, and which is deleted in the manuscript: "And so, in order to find this ratio, we must proceed to the cause of speed and slowness of motion. The stronger the cause, the stronger will be the effect. Thus, a greater, that is, a swifter, motion will result from a greater weight, and a slower motion from a smaller weight. We say that the ratio of the speeds of motion of bodies is the same as the ratio of the weights, provided they are weighed in the medium in which the motion is to take place. Note this proviso. Otherwise one might weigh two spheres in air, one of iron, the other of wood, and find that the iron sphere is ten times as heavy as the wooden one; and, then, on lowering both into water, find that the iron sphere sinks, while the wooden one does not. Thus there would be no ratio [of the speeds] of motion of the iron and the wood. Bodies must therefore be weighed in the medium in which the motion is to take place. For the ratio of the weights of two bodies is not the same in different media. But a very great difficulty arises here. For we find in experience that if two spheres of equal size, one of which is double the other in weight, are dropped from a tower, the heavier one does not reach the ground twice as quickly. Indeed, at the beginning of the motion the lighter one will move ahead of the heavier, and for some distance will move more swiftly than it. This is something that demands attention and is very important, but since it depends on matters we have not yet explained, its discussion will be postponed until the discussion of the reason for the increase in the speed of natural motion. There it will be shown that it is *per accidens* that natural motion is slower in the

tion to Aristotle's view, that also for bodies of *different* material this ratio is not equal to the ratio of their weights, we shall prove certain propositions. On these depends the outcome not only of this investigation but also of the investigation of the ratio of the speeds of the same body moving in different media. And we shall consider both matters together.

268   Let us therefore proceed to investigate the ratio [of the speeds] of the same body moving in different media. And first let us examine whether or not Aristotle's view on this is sounder than the other view explained above. Now Aristotle held that in the case of the same body moving in different media the ratio of the speeds was equal to the ratio of the rarenesses[13] of the media. Indeed, that is what he wrote quite clearly, saying (*Physics* 4.71):[14] "That medium which is denser interferes with motion more. Thus *a* will move over path *b* in time *c,* and over path *d,* a rarer medium, in time *e,* [the times being] in the ratio of the hindering action of the media, provided the lengths of the paths are equal. Thus, if *b* is water and *d* air, *a* will move through *d* more swiftly than through *b* in proportion as air is less dense than water. Thus speed has to speed the same ratio as that between air and water. That is, if air is twice as rare as water, *a* will take twice as long to traverse path *b* as to traverse path *d;* and time *c* will be twice time *e.*"

These are Aristotle's words, but surely they embrace a false viewpoint. And to make this perfectly clear I shall construct the following proof. If the ratio of the speeds is equal to the ratio of the rarenesses of the media, let there be a moving body *o* and a medium *a,* whose rareness is 4; let this medium be water, for example. Let the rareness of medium *b* be 16, greater, that is, than the rareness of *a;* and let us say, for example, that *b* is air. Now suppose that body *o* is such that it does not sink in water, but suppose that its velocity in medium *b* is 8. Hence, since the speed of *o* in medium *b* is 8, but in medium *a* is zero, some medium can surely be found in which the speed of *o* is 1. Let such a medium be *c.* Now since *o* moves more swiftly in medium *b* than in *c,* the

beginning, from which it will follow that it is also *per accidens* that a body twice as heavy does not fall twice as fast from a tower. And the reason will also then be given why, at the beginning of the motion, the lighter body moves more swiftly than the heavier one. Let this suffice for now on the ratio [of the speeds] of motion of different bodies moving in the same medium" (F). [Cf. ch. 22, below.]

13. Galileo uses "rareness" as the inverse of density, so that "ratio of rarenesses" is the same as "inverse ratio of densities."

14. 215a29–b10.

rareness of *c* must be less than the rareness of *b,* and it
269   must, according to our adversary, be less in proportion
as the speed in medium *c* is less than the speed in
medium *b.* But the speed in medium *b* was assumed to be eight
times the speed in medium *c.* Therefore the rareness of medium
b will be eight times the rareness of medium *c.* Hence the rareness of *c* will be 2. Therefore, *o* moves with speed 1 in the rareness of medium *c,* which is 2. But it was assumed that it cannot
move in the rareness of medium *a,* which is 4.[15] Hence *o* will fail
to move in the medium of greater rareness, though it moves in
the medium of lesser rareness. This is completely absurd. Clearly,
then, the speeds of the motions are not in the same ratio as the
rarenesses of the media.

But even apart from other proof, can anyone fail to see the
error in Aristotle's opinion? For if the speeds have the same ratio
as the [rarenesses of the] media, then, conversely, the [rarenesses
of the] media will have the same ratio as the speeds. Hence, since
wood falls in air but not in water, and, consequently, the speed
in air has no ratio to the speed in water, it follows that the rareness of air will have no ratio to the rareness of water. What can
be more absurd than this? But someone might think that he
would be giving a sufficient answer to my argument, if he said:
"Though wood does not move downward in water, it does move
upward; and the rareness of water has to the rareness of air the
same ratio as the speed of the motion upward in water has to the
speed of the motion downward in air." And he might believe that
he had skillfully saved Aristotle by such an answer. But we shall
destroy this subterfuge, too, by considering a body which moves
neither up nor down in water. Such a body, for example, would
be water itself. But water moves in air with considerable speed.

And so, having properly rejected Aristotle's view, let us now
investigate the ratio [of the speeds] of the motion of the same
body in different media. And first, in connection with upward
motion, let us show that, when solids lighter than water are completely immersed in water, they are carried upward with a force
measured by the difference between the weight of a volume of
water equal to the volume of the submerged body and the weight
of the body itself.[16] Thus, let the first position of the water, before

15. A velocity of zero in water would, in Aristotle's view, imply a rareness of
zero for the medium, so that Galileo's assumption of a rareness of 4 would not
be in order. But, in any case, the notion of zero rareness (or infinite density) for
water must lead to anomalous results, as Galileo points out below.
16. Where are the weighings to be made? It will avoid the problem of nega-

the body is immersed in it, have as its surface *ab;* and let the
solid *cd* be forcibly immersed in it, the surface of the water being
raised to *ef.* Since the raised water *eb* has a volume equal to that
of the whole submerged body, and the body is assumed to be
lighter than water, the weight of the water *eb* will be greater than
the weight of *cd.* Then let *tb* represent that part of the water
whose weight is equal to the weight of body *cd.* We must therefore prove that body *cd* is carried upward with a force equal to the

270
weight of *tf* (for this is the amount by which water *eb* is
heavier than water *tb,* that is to say, than body *cd*).

Now since the weight of water *tb* is equal to the weight
of *cd,* water *tb* will press upward so as to raise *cd* with the same
force with which that body will resist being raised. Thus the
weight of a part of the water that exerts pressure, namely *tb,* is
equal to the resistance of the solid body. But the weight of all the
water that exerts pressure, namely *eb,* exceeds the weight of water
tb by the weight of water *tf.* Thus the weight of all the water *eb*
will exceed the resistance of solid *cd* by the weight of water *tf.*
Therefore the weight of all the water that exerts pressure will impel the solid upward with a force equal to the weight of part *tf* of
the water. Which was to be proved.

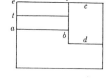

From this proof, first, it is clear that upward motion results
from the weight not merely of the body, but of the medium, as
we have shown; and, secondly, the whole purpose of our investigation can be achieved. For since we are investigating how much
faster the same body rises in one medium than in another, whenever we know how fast it moves through each medium, we shall
also know the interval between the two speeds. And this is what
we seek. If, for example, a piece of wood whose weight is 4 moves
upward in water, and the weight of a volume of water equal to
that of the wood is 6, the wood will move with a speed that we
may represent as 2. But if, now, the same piece of wood is carried
upward in a medium heavier than water, a medium such that a
volume of it equal to the volume of the wood has a weight of 10,
the wood will rise in this medium with a speed that we may
represent as 6. But it moved in the other medium with a speed 2.
Therefore the two speeds will be to each other as 6 and 2, and
not (as Aristotle held) as the weights or densities of the media,
which are to each other as 10 and 6. It is clear, then, that in all
cases the speeds of upward motion are to each other as the ex-

tive weights if the medium of weighing is no heavier than any of the objects
weighed.

cess of weight of one medium[17] over the weight of the moving body is to the excess of weight of the other medium over the weight of the body.

Therefore, if we wish to know at once the [relative] speeds of a given body in two different media, we take an amount of each medium equal to the volume of the body, and subtract from the weights [of such amounts] of each medium the weight of the body. The numbers found as remainders will be to each other as the speeds of the motions.[18]

271

And we also obtain the answer to our second problem, namely, the ratio of the speeds[19] of different bodies equal in volume but unequal in weight. For if each of them moves upward with a force measured by the difference between the weight of a volume of the medium equal to the volume of the body and the weight of the body itself, the numerical remainders, when the weights of the various bodies are subtracted from the weight of the aforesaid volume of the medium, will have the same ratio as the speeds. For example, if the weight of one body is 4, of a second body 6, and of the medium 8, the speed of the body whose weight is 4 will be 4, and the speed of the other body will be 2. These speeds, 4 and 2, do not have the same ratio, as the lightnesses of the bodies, 6 and 4.[20] For the excesses of one number over two others will never have the same ratio to each other as the two numbers themselves; nor will the excesses of two numbers over another number have the same ratio to each other as the two numbers themselves.[21] It is therefore clear that in motion upward the speeds of the different bodies are not in the same ratio as the lightnesses of the bodies.

It remains for us to show that also in the [natural] downward motion of bodies the ratio of the speeds is not equal to the ratio of the weights of the bodies; and at the same time to determine the ratio of the speeds of the same body moving in different media. All these results will easily be drawn from the following demonstration. I say, then, that a solid body heavier than water moves downward [in water] with a force measured by the difference in weight between an amount of water equal to the vol-

---

17. I.e., the weight of a volume of it equal to the volume of the moving body.

18. Benedetti, *Diversarum speculationum . . . liber* (note 9, above), p. 169, formulated it thus: "that the speeds of natural motion of a heavy body in different media are proportional to the weights of that body in the respective media" (cited by A. Koyré, *Études Galiléennes,* I, 49).

19. I.e., of natural motion in the same medium.

20. Since the weights of the bodies were 4 and 6, respectively, Galileo refers to their lightnesses as 6 and 4, respectively.

21. Provided the two numbers are unequal.

ume of the solid body and the body itself. Thus, let the water in its first position have the surface *de;* and let solid *bl,* heavier than water, be let down into it, the surface of the water rising to *ab,* so that water *ae* has a volume equal to the volume of the solid itself. Since the solid is assumed to be heavier than water, the weight of the water [*ae*] will be less than the weight of the solid. Thus, let *ao* be an amount of water that has a weight equal to the weight of *bl.* Now, since water *ae* is lighter than *ao* by the weight of *do,* we must prove that body *bl* moves downward with a force measured by the weight of water *do.*

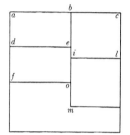

272   Imagine a second solid body, lighter than water and joined to the first body; let its volume be equal to that of water *ao* and its weight equal to the weight of water *ae.* Let *lm* represent this body. Since the volume of *bl* is equal to that of *ae,* and the volume of *lm* is equal to that of *ao,* the volume of the combined bodies, *bl* and *lm,* is equal to the sum of the volumes of *ea* and *ao.* But the weight of water *ae* is equal to the weight of body *lm;* and the weight of water *ao* is equal to the weight of body *bl.* Therefore the whole weight of both bodies, *bl* and *lm,* is equal to the weight of water *oa* and *ae.* But the volume of the [combined] bodies [*bl* and *lm*] has been shown to be equal to the [combined] volume of water *oa* and *ae.* Hence by our first proposition, the bodies so joined will neither rise nor sink. Therefore the force of the downward pressure of body *bl* will be equal to the force of the upward pressure of *lm.* But, by the foregoing demonstration, magnitude *lm* tends to move upward with a force equal to the weight of water *do.* Therefore body *bl* will move downward with a force equal to the weight of water *do.* Which was to be proved.

Now if this demonstration is grasped, the answer to our problems can easily be discerned. For, clearly, in the case of the same body falling in different media, the ratio of the speeds of the motions is the same as the ratio of the amounts by which the weight of the body exceeds the weights [of an equal volume] of the respective media. Thus, if the weight of the body is 8, and the weight of a volume of one medium equal to the volume of the body is 6, the speed of the body can be represented by 2. And if the weight of a volume of the second medium equal to the volume of the body is 4, the speed of the body in this second medium can be represented by 4. Clearly, then, these speeds will be to each other as 2 and 4, and not as the densities or weights of the media, as Aristotle believed, i.e., as 6 and 4.[22]

22. It would have been more exact to say "as 4 and 6," taking the first me-

And similarly we have a clear answer to our second problem—
to find the ratio of the speeds of bodies equal in size, but unequal
in weight, moving [with natural motion] in the same medium.
For the speeds of these bodies have the same ratio as do the
amounts by which the weights of the bodies exceed the weight
of the medium. For example, if there are two bodies equal in volume but unequal in weight, the weight of one of them being 8, and
of the other 6, and if the weight of a volume of the me-
273   dium equal to the volume of either body is 4, the speed
of the first body will be 4 and of the second 2. These
speeds will have a ratio of 4 to 2, not the same as the ratio between
their weights, which is 8 to 6.

And from all that has been said here, it will not be difficult also
to find the ratio in the case of bodies of different material moving
in different media. For we examine first the ratio of the speeds
of both bodies in the same medium. How this is to be done is
clear from what has already been said. Then we consider what
speed [the appropriate] one of the bodies has in the second
medium (again with the help of what has been stated above):
and we shall then have what is sought. For example, suppose
there are two bodies, equal in size but unequal in weight, the
weight of one being 12, and of the other 8, and we seek the
ratio between the speed of the one whose weight is 12 sinking in
water, and the speed of the one whose weight is 8 falling in air.
Consider first how much faster the body weighing 12 sinks in
water than the body weighing 8; then how much faster the body
weighing 8 moves in air than in water, and we shall have what
we are looking for. Or, alternatively, consider how much more
swiftly the body weighing 12 falls in air than the body weighing 8; and then how much more slowly the body weighing 12
moves in water than in air.[23]

These, then, are the general rules governing the ratio of the
speeds of [natural] motion of bodies made of the same or of different material, in the same medium or in different media, and
moving upward or downward. But note that a great difficulty
arises at this point, because those ratios will not be observable by
one who makes the experiment. For if one takes two different
bodies, which have such properties that the first should fall twice

---

dium first. Aristotle held the speed to be *inversely* proportional to the density
of the medium.

23. $v_{am}/v_{bn} = (v_{am}/v_{bm}) \times (v_{bm}/v_{bn})$, where v_{am} is the speed of body a in
medium m, etc. The method of finding the ratios in the right-hand member has
previously been discussed.

as fast as the second, and if one then lets them fall from a tower, the first will not reach the ground appreciably faster or twice as fast. Indeed, if an observation is made, the lighter body will, at the beginning of the motion, move ahead of the heavier and will be swifter.[24] This is not the place to consider how these contradictory and, so to speak, unnatural accidents come about (for they are accidental). In fact, certain things must be considered first which have not yet been examined. For we must first consider why natural motion is slower at its beginning.

24. See ch. 22.

Chapter [9]

In which all that was demonstrated above is considered in physical terms, and bodies moving naturally are reduced to the weights of a balance.

When a person has discovered the truth about something and has established it with great effort, then, on viewing his discoveries more carefully, he often realizes that what he has taken such pains to find might have been perceived with the greatest ease. For truth has the property that it is not so deeply concealed as many have thought; indeed, its traces shine brightly in various places and there are many paths by which it is approached. Yet it often happens that we do not see what is quite near at hand and clear. And we have a clear example of this right before us. For everything that was demonstrated and explained above so laboriously is shown us by nature so openly and clearly that nothing could be plainer or more obvious.

That this may be clear to everyone, let us consider how and why bodies moving upward [in natural motion] move with a force measured by the amount by which the weight of a volume of the medium (through which motion takes place) equal to the volume of the moving body exceeds the weight of the body itself. Consider a piece of wood that rises in water and floats on the surface. Now it is clear that the wood moves upward with just as much force as is necessary to submerge it forcibly in the water. If, therefore, we can find how much force is necessary to hold the wood under the water, we shall have what we are looking for. But if the wood were not lighter than water, that is, if its weight were the same as the weight of a volume of water equal to the volume of the wood, it would, of course, remain submerged, and it would not rise above the surface of the water. Therefore a force

equal to the amount by which the weight of the aforesaid volume
of water exceeds the weight of the piece of wood is sufficient to
submerge the piece of wood. That is, we have found how much
weight is required to submerge the piece of wood. But it was just
determined that the wood moves upward with a force equal to
that required to submerge it. And the weight just now found is
what is required to submerge it. Therefore the wood moves upward with a force measured by the amount by which the weight
of a volume of water equal to the volume of the wood exceeds
the weight of the wood. And this is what was sought.

    We must deal with downward motion by like reasoning. Thus
we ask with what force a lead sphere moves downward in water. Now it is clear, to begin with, that the
lead sphere moves downward with as much force as
would be required to draw it upward. But if the sphere were
made of water instead of lead, no force would be necessary to
draw it upward, or, more precisely, the very smallest of forces.
Therefore a weight equal to the amount by which the lead
sphere exceeds an aqueous sphere of the same size measures the
resistance of the lead sphere to being drawn upward. But the
lead sphere also moves downward with the same force with
which it resists being drawn upward. Therefore the lead sphere
moves downward with a force equal to the weight by which it
exceeds the weight of an aqueous sphere [of the same size].

    One can see this same thing in the weights of a scale. For if the
weights are in balance, and an additional weight is added to one
side, then that side moves down, not in consequence of its whole
weight, but only by reason of the weight by which it exceeds the
weight on the other side. That is the same as if we were to say
that the weight on this side moves down with a force measured
by the amount by which the weight on the other side is less than
it. And, for the same reason, the weight on the other side will
move up with a force measured by the amount by which the
weight on the first side is greater than it.

    From what was said in this and in the previous chapter, we
have the general conclusion that in the case of bodies of different
material, provided that they are equal in size, the ratio of the
speeds of their [natural downward] motions is the same as
the ratio of their weights—and not their weights as such, but the
weights found by weighing them in the medium in which the
motion is to take place.[1] Consider, for example, two bodies, *a* and

275

---

    1. To include natural upward motion the formulation would properly refer to
relative lightness or negative weights.

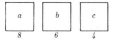

b, equal in size but not in weight. Let the weight in air of *a* be 8 and of *b* 6. The speeds [of the natural motion] of these bodies in water will not, as has been said before, have the ratio 8 to 6. For if we take a volume of water *c* equal to the volume of the bodies, and its weight is 4, the speed of body *a* will be represented by 4, and the speed of *b* by 2. And these speeds are in the ratio of 2 to 1, not in the ratio of 4 to 3, the ratio of the weights of the bodies in air. Yet the weights of these same bodies in water will also be in the ratio of 2 to 1; for the weight of *a* in water would only be 4.

This can be made clear as follows. If the weight of *a* in air were 4, it would be zero in water. For *a* would then be of the same weight as water, since 4 was assumed to be the weight in air of a volume of water *c* equal to the volume of *a*. But the weight of *c* in water would be zero, for it would move neither up-
276   ward nor downward. Therefore the weight of *a* in water would be zero, if it were 4 in air. But because it is 8 in air, it will be 4 in water; and, by the same reasoning, the weight of *b* in water would be 2. Therefore their weights would be in the ratio of 2 to 1, as are also the speeds of their motions. And one must deal with lightness by a similar argument.

Now we conclude that, given the weights of two bodies in air, their weights in water can be found immediately. For having subtracted from each the weight of a volume of water equal to the volume of the solid bodies, we shall have as remainders the weights of these bodies in water. And similarly with other media.

Now from what has been said it should be clear to everyone that we do not have for any object its own proper weight. For if two objects are weighed, let us say, in water, who can say that the weights which we then obtain are the true weights of these objects, when, if these same objects are weighed in air, the weights will prove to be different from those [found in water] and will have a different ratio to each other? And if these objects could again be weighed in still another medium, e.g., fire, the weights would once more be different, and would have a dif-ferent ratio to each other. And in this way the weights will always vary, along with the differences of the media. But if the objects could be weighed in a void, then we surely would find their exact weights, when no weight of the medium would diminish the weight of the objects. However, since the Peripa-tetics, following their leader, have said that in a void no motions could take place, and that therefore all things would be equally heavy, perhaps it will not be inappropriate to examine this opinion and to consider its foundations and its proofs. For this problem is one of the things that have to do with motion.

Chapter [10]

In which, in opposition to Aristotle, it is proved that, if there were a void, motion in it would not take place instantaneously, but in time.

Aristotle, in Book 4 of the *Physics,* in his attempt to deny the existence of a void adduces many arguments. Those that are found beginning with section 64[1] are drawn from a consideration of motion. For since he assumes that motion cannot take place instantaneously, he tries to show that if a void existed, motion in it would take place instantaneously; and, since that is impossible, he concludes necessarily that a void is also impossible. But, since we are dealing with motion, we have decided to in-277   quire whether it is true that, if a void existed, motion in it would take place instantaneously. And since our conclusion will be that motion in a void takes place in time, we shall first examine the contrary view and Aristotle's arguments.

In the first place, of the arguments adduced by Aristotle there is none that involves a necessary conclusion, but there is one which, at first sight, seems to lead to such a conclusion. This is the argument set forth in sections 71 and 72,[2] in which Aristotle deduces the following inconsistency—that, on the assumption that motion can take place in time in a void, then the same body will move in the same time in a plenum and in a void. In order to be better able to refute this argument, we have decided to state it at this point.

Thus, Aristotle's first assumption, when he saw that the same body moved more swiftly through the rarer than through the denser medium, was this: that the ratio of the speed of motion in one medium to the speed in the second medium is equal to the ratio of the rareness of the first medium to the rareness of the second.[3] He then reasoned as follows. Suppose body a traverses medium b in time c, and that it traverses a medium rarer than b, namely d, in time e. Clearly, the ratio of time c to time e is equal to the ratio of the density of b to the density of d. Suppose, then, that there is a void f and that body a traverses f, if it is possible,

1. 214a27 ff.
2. 215b–216a.
3. See ch. 8, note 13, above.

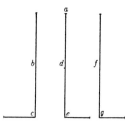

not in an instant, but in time g. And suppose that the ratio of the density of medium d to the density of some new medium is equal to the ratio of time e to time g. Then, from what has been established, body a will move through the new medium in time g, since [the density of] medium d has to that of the new medium the same ratio as time e to time g. But in the same time g body a also moves through the void f. Therefore a will in the same time move over two equal paths, one a plenum, the other a void. But this is impossible. Therefore the body will not move through the void in time; and therefore the motion will be instantaneous.

Such is Aristotle's proof. And, indeed, his conclusions would have been sound and necessary, if he had proved his assumptions, or at least if these assumptions, even though unproved, had been true. But he was deceived in this, that he assumed as well-recognized axioms propositions which not only are not obvious to the senses, but have never been proved, and cannot be proved because they are completely false. For he assumed that the ratio of the speeds of the same body moving in different media is equal to the ratio of the rarenesses of the media. But that this is false has been fully proved above.[4] In support of that proof, I shall add only this. Suppose it is true that the ratio of the rareness of air to the rareness of water is equal to the ratio of the speed of a body moving in air to the speed of the same body in water. Then, when a drop or some other quantity of water falls swiftly in air, but does not fall at all in water, since the speed in air has no ratio to the speed in water, it follows, according to Aristotle himself, that there will be no ratio between the rareness of air and the rareness of water. But that is ridiculous.[5]

Therefore, it is clear that, when Aristotle argues in this way, we must answer him as follows. In the first place, as has been shown above, it is not true that differences in the slowness and speed of a given body arise from the greater or lesser density and rareness of the medium. But even if that were conceded, it is still not true that the ratio of the speeds of the motion of the body is equal to the ratio of the rarenesses of the media.

And as for Aristotle's statement in the same section that it is

278

4. 268–69.

5. There is the following marginal addition at this point: "If this were true, the ratio of the speed of motion in air to the speed of motion in water would be the same for all bodies. Hence the ratio of the speed of lead in air to its speed in water would be the same as the ratio of the speed of wood in air to its speed in water. But who cannot see that this is false? For lead sinks in water, wood does not" (F).

impossible for one number to have the same relation[6] to another
number as a number has to zero, this is, of course, true of geometric ratios [viz., a/b], and not merely in numbers but in every
kind of quantity. Since, in the case of geometric ratios, it is necessarily true that the smaller magnitude can be added to itself a
sufficient number of times so that it will ultimately exceed any
magnitude whatever, it follows that this smaller magnitude is
something, and not zero. For zero, no matter how often it is
added to itself, will exceed no quantity. But Aristotle's conclusion
does not apply to *arithmetic* relations [viz., the difference, $a - b$].
That is, in these cases, one number can have the same relation to
another number as still another number has to zero. For, since
[two pairs of] numbers are in the same arithmetic relation when
the difference of the [two] larger is equal to the difference of the
[two] smaller,[7] it will, of course, be possible for one number to
have the same [arithmetic] relation to another number, as still
another number has to zero. Thus, we say that the [arithmetic]
relation of 20 to 12 is the same as that of 8 to 0: for
279   the excess of 20 over 12, i.e., 8, is equal to the excess
of 8 over 0.

Therefore, if, as Aristotle held, the ratio of the speeds were
equal to the ratio, in the geometric sense, of the rarenesses of the
media, Aristotle's conclusion would have been valid, that motion
in a void could not take place in time. For the ratio of the time
in the plenum to the time in the void cannot be equal to the ratio
of the rareness of the plenum to the rareness of the void,[8] since
the rareness of the void does not exist.[9] But if the ratio of the
speeds were made to depend on the aforesaid ratio, not in the
geometric, but in the arithmetic sense [i.e., as a ratio of differ-
ences], no absurd conclusion would follow. And, in fact, the
ratio of the speeds does depend, in an arithmetic sense, on the
relation of the lightness of the first medium to that of the second.
For the ratio of the speeds is equal, not to the ratio of the lightness of the first medium to that of the second, but, as has been

6. Galileo's point depends on the two senses of this word (*proportio*). Aristotle's conclusion is sound for what Galileo here calls a geometric *proportio* (i.e.,
the ratio a/b), but not for an arithmetic *proportio* (i.e., the difference, $a - b$).

7. Or, what is equivalent, the difference between the two members of each pair
is equal.

8. There seems to be a slip here. Galileo may have meant to say "density"
instead of "rareness" (see the next note). The same effect would have been
achieved by saying "ratio of the rareness of the *void* to the rareness of the
plenum" or by speaking of the ratio of *speeds,* not of times.

9. In the sense of being greater than any finite number. But Galileo may
have meant to speak of density, in which case *nulla* would be "zero."

proved, to the ratio of the excess of the weight of the body over the weight of the first medium to the excess of the weight of the body over the weight of the second medium.

So that this may be clearer, here is an example. Suppose there is a body *a* whose weight is 20, and two media unequal in weight, *bc* and *de*. Let the volume of *b* be equal to that of *a,* and the volume of *d* also equal to that of *a*. Since we are now discussing downward motion that takes place in a void, let the media be lighter than the body *a,* and let the weight of *b* be 12, and of *d* 6. It is clear, then, from what was proved above, that the ratio of the speed of body *a* in medium *bc* to the speed of the same body in medium *de* will be equal to the ratio of the excess of the weight of *a* over the weight of *b* to the excess of the weight of *a* over the weight of *d,* that is, as 8 is to 14. Thus if the speed of *a* in medium *bc* is 8, its speed in medium *de* would be 14. Now it is clear that the ratio of the speeds, 14 to 8, is not the same as the ratio (in the geometric sense) of the lightness of one medium to the lightness of the other. For the lightness of medium *de* is double that of medium *bc* (for since the weight of *b* is 12, and of *d* 6,

280   i.e., since the weight of *b* is double the weight of *d,* the lightness of *d* will be double the lightness of *b*); but a speed of 14 is less than twice a speed of 8. Yet the speed 14 has to the speed 8 the same relation, in the arithmetic sense, as the lightness of *d* to the lightness of *b,* since the difference between 14 and 8 is 6, and 6 is also the difference between the lightness of *d* (12) and the lightness of *b* (6).[10]

Furthermore, if medium *de* should be lighter, so that the weight of *d* is 5, the speed *f* will be 15 (for 15 will be the difference between the weight of body *a* and the weight of the medium *d*). And again the relation [i.e., arithmetic difference] of speed 15 and speed 8 will be the same as between the weight of medium *b* (12) and the weight of medium *d* (5), that is, the same as the relation of the lightness of *d* and the lightness of *b*. For the difference in each case will be 7. Furthermore, if the weight of *d* is only 4, the speed *f* will be 16: and the relation of speed 16 and speed 8 (with a difference of 8) is the same arithmetic relation as between the weight of *b* (12) and the weight of *d* (4), i.e., between the lightness of *d* and the lightness of *b,* the difference being also 8. If, again, medium *de* becomes lighter, and the weight of *d* is only 3, the speed *f* will now be 17. And between the speed

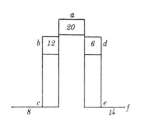

---

10. If the weights of *d* and *b* are 6 and 12, respectively, Galileo here speaks of their lightnesses as 12 and 6, respectively, with difference 6. And similarly in what follows.

f (17) and the speed 8 (a difference of 9), the difference is the same as between the weight of *b* (12) and the weight of *d* (3), i.e., as between the lightness of *d* and the lightness of *b*. If, again, medium *de* becomes lighter, and the weight of *d* is only 2, the speed *f* will now be 18. And the arithmetic difference between that speed and the speed 8 will be the same as the difference between the weight of *b* (12) and the weight of *d* (2), i.e., between the lightness of *d* and the lightness of *b*. In each case the difference will be 10. If, again, medium *de* becomes lighter, and the weight of *d* is only 1, the speed *f* will now be 19. And there will be the same arithmetic difference between this speed and the speed 8 as between the weight of *b* (12) and the weight of *d* (1), i.e., between the lightness of *d* and the lightness of *b*. In each case the difference will be 11. Now if, finally, the weight of *d* is 0, so that the difference between the weight of body *a* and of the medium *d* is 20, the speed *f* will be 20; and the arithmetic difference between the speed *f* (20) and the speed 8 will be the same as that between the weight of *b* (12) and the weight of *d* (0), the difference in each case being 12.

It is clear, therefore, that the relation of speed to speed is the same as the relation of the lightness of one medium to the lightness of the other, not geometrically [i.e., as a quotient] but arithmetically [i.e., as a difference]. And since it is not absurd for this arithmetic relation [i.e., difference] to be the same between one quantity and a second quantity as between a third quantity and zero, it will similarly not be absurd for the relation of speed to speed to be the same, in this arithmetic sense, as the relation of a given lightness [of medium] to zero.

281

Therefore, the body will move in a void in the same way as in a plenum. For in a plenum the speed of motion of a body depends on the difference between its weight and the weight of the medium through which it moves. And likewise in a void [the speed of] its motion will depend on the difference between its own weight and that of the medium. But since the latter is zero, the difference between the weight of the body and the weight of the void will be the whole weight of the body. And therefore the speed of its motion [in the void] will depend on its own total weight.[11] But in no plenum will it be able to move so quickly, since the excess of the weight of the body over the weight of the medium is less than the whole weight of the body. Therefore its

---

11. I.e., its weight in the void, undiminished by any weight of medium.

speed will be less than if it moved according to its own total weight.

From this it can clearly be understood that in a plenum, such as that which surrounds us, things do not weigh their proper and natural weight, but they will always be lighter to the extent that they are in a heavier medium. Indeed, a body will be lighter by an amount equal to the weight, in a void, of a volume of the medium equal to the volume of the body. Thus, a lead sphere will be lighter in water than in a void by an amount equal to the weight, in a void, of an aqueous sphere of the same size as the lead sphere. And the lead sphere is lighter in air than in a void by an amount equal to the weight, in a void, of a sphere of air having the same size as the lead sphere. And so also in fire, and in other media. And since the speed of a body's motion depends on the weight the body has in the medium in which it moves, its motion will be swifter, the heavier the body is in relation to the various media.

But the following argument is invalid: "A void is a medium infinitely lighter than every plenum; therefore motion in it will be infinitely swifter than in a plenum; therefore such motion will be instantaneous." For it is true that a void is infinitely lighter than any [nonvacuous] medium; but we must not say that such a [nonvacuous] medium is of infinite weight. We must instead understand [the applicability of the term "infinite"] in this way, that between the lightness of air, for example, and a void there may exist an unlimited number of media lighter than air and heavier than a void. And if we understand the matter in this way, there may also exist, between the speed in air and the speed in a void, an unlimited number of speeds, greater than the speed in air and less than the speed in a void. And so also between the weight of a body in air and its weight in a void, an unlimited number of intermediate weights may exist, greater than the weight of the body in air, but less than its weight in a void.[12]

282

And the same is true of every continuum. Thus between lines a and b, of which a is greater, an unlimited number of intermediate lines, smaller than a, but greater than b may exist (for since the amount by which a exceeds b is also a line, it will be infinitely divisible). But we must not say that line a is infinitely greater than line b, in the sense that even if b were to be added to itself without limit, it would not produce a line greater than a. And by

12. Reading *vacuo* instead of *medio* (282.1). Galileo may have inadvertently written the latter under the influence of *mediae* of the preceding line.

similar reasoning, if we suppose a to be the speed in a void, and b the speed in air, an unlimited number of speeds, greater than b and smaller than a, will be able to exist between a and b. Yet we must not conclude that a is infinitely greater than b, in the sense that the time in which [the motion with] speed a is accomplished, when added to itself any number of times without limit, can still never exceed the time corresponding to speed b, and that, therefore, the speed corresponding to time a is instantaneous.

It is therefore clear how the argument is to be understood. "The lightness of a void infinitely exceeds the lightness of a [non-vacuous] medium; therefore the speed in the void will infinitely exceed the speed in a plenum." All that is conceded. What is denied is the conclusion: "Therefore the speed [i.e., the motion] in the void will be instantaneous." For such motion can take place in time, but in a shorter time than the time corresponding to the speed in a plenum; so that between the time in the plenum and the time in the void an unlimited number of times, greater than the latter and smaller than the former, may exist. Hence it follows, not that motion in a void is instantaneous, but that it takes place in less time than the time of motion in any plenum.

Therefore, to put it briefly, my whole point is this. Suppose there is a heavy body a, whose proper and natural weight[13] is 1000. Its weight in any plenum whatever will be less than 1000, and therefore the speed of its motion in any plenum will be less than 1000. Thus if we assume a medium such that the weight of a volume of it equal to the volume of a is only 1, then the weight of a in this medium will be 999. Therefore its speed too will be 999. And the speed of a will be 1000 only in a medium in which its weight is 1000, and that will be nowhere except in a void.

This is the refutation of Aristotle's argument. And from this refutation it can readily be seen that motion in a void does not have to be instantaneous. The other arguments of Aristotle are without force or cogency. To say, for example, that in a void the body will not move in one direction rather than in another, or up rather than down, because the void does not give

way upward or downward but equally in all directions,[14] is childish. For I could say the same thing about air. That is, when a stone is in air, how does the air give way downward rather than upward, or to the left rather than to the right, if the rareness of the air is everywhere the same? At this point someone, quoting Aristotle,[15] might say that

---

13. I.e., its weight in a void.   14. Cf. *Physics* 215a22–24.
15. Cf. *De Caelo* 311b9.

air has weight in its own place and therefore helps downward
motion more. We shall examine these fantasies in the next chapter, where we shall investigate whether elements have weight in
their own proper places. And similarly, when they say that in a
void there is neither up nor down, who dreamt this up? If the
air were a void, would not the void near the earth be nearer the
center than the void which is near [the region of] fire?

Similarly lacking in force is the argument which Aristotle
makes about projectiles when he says:[16] "Projectiles cannot move
in a void, for projectiles, when they have left the hand of the
thrower, are moved by the air or by some other corporeal
medium that surrounds them and is set in motion. But this is not
present in a void." For Aristotle assumes that projectiles are
carried along by the medium; and in the proper place we shall
show that this is false.[17] And what he adds to his argument,
about different bodies moving in the same medium, is also false.
For he assumes that in a plenum heavier bodies move more
swiftly because they cleave the medium more forcibly, and that
this is the only reason for their speed; but since that resistance is
not present in a void, he supposes that all motions in a void will
take place in the same time and with the same speed—and this,
he asserts, is impossible.[18]

Now, in the first place, Aristotle errs in that he does not prove
that it is absurd for different bodies to move in a void with the
same speed. But he makes an even greater error when he assumes
that the speeds of different bodies depend on an ability of heavier
bodies to divide the medium better. For, as we showed above, the
speed of moving bodies does not depend on this, but on the size
of the difference between the weight of the bodies and the weight
of the medium. For the speeds are in the ratio of these differences.
But the difference between the weights of different bodies and
the weight of the same medium is not the same (for otherwise the
bodies would be equally heavy). Therefore the speeds will not be
equal. For example, in the case of a body whose weight is 8, the
excess over the weight of the void (which is 0) is 8; hence its
speed will be 8. But if the weight of a body is 4, the excess over
the [weight of the] void will, in the same way, be 4; and hence
its speed will be 4. Finally, using the same method of
proof in the case of the void as we used in the case of
the plenum,[19] we can show that bodies of the same

284

16. Cf. *Physics* 215a14–19.
17. Cf. ch. 17, below.
18. *Physics* 216a12–21.
19. See 265, above.

material but of different size move with the same speed in a void. So much for that.

Such[20] is the force of truth that learned men, even Peripatetics, have recognized that Aristotle's view on this subject was mistaken, though none of them could properly refute his arguments. And, as for what is contained in *Physics* 4.71–72,[21] certainly no one was ever able to refute that argument, for up to now the fallacy in it has never been noticed. And though Scotus, Saint Thomas, Philoponus,[22] and some others hold a view opposed to Aristotle's, they arrive at the truth by belief rather than real proof or by refuting Aristotle. And, indeed, if one were to accept Aristotle's assumption about the ratio of the speeds of the same body moving in different media, one could scarcely hope to be able to refute Aristotle and upset his proof. For Aristotle assumes that the speed in one medium is to the speed in the other, as the rareness of the first medium is to the rareness of the second. And no one up to now has ventured to deny this relation.[23]

Nor is there any validity in the assumption made by the aforesaid writers, namely, a twofold resistance to the motion of the body—one external, resulting from the density of the medium, the other internal, by reason of the determinate weight of the body. For there is something artificial about this; since those two resistances do not, if we look at the matter carefully, differ from each other. For, as has been made clear above, the density or (to use a better term) the weight of the medium makes for lightness of the moving body, and the lightness of the medium is responsible for the heaviness of the body; and the same body is now

20. This section to the end of the chapter is on a separate sheet. Galileo merely indicated that it belongs in this chapter; and Favaro placed it at the end of the chapter.

21. 215b–216a.

22. Ioannes Duns Scotus, *Opera Omnia* III (Paris, 1891), 102–3 (on Arist. *Phys.* 4. Quaest 12.18,19); D. Thomas Aquinas, *Opera* III (Rome, 1884), 186. *Comm. on Arist. Phys.* IV. ch. 8. lectio 12, no. 8; Ioannes Philoponus, *Comm. in Phys. Arist.*, pp. 678–84 (Vitelli).

23. But Philoponus, cited above by Galileo, *does* deny the relation as it is expressed in the form "time required in one medium is to time required in the other medium as density of first medium is to density of the second." Cf. *Commentary on Aristotle's Physics*, p. 682.30–32 (Vitelli). G. B. Benedetti also denies the relation (*Diversarum speculationum mathematicarum et physicarum liber* [Turin, 1585], p. 172; see A. Koyré, *Études Galiléennes*, I, 50). From what Galileo says one may question how much direct and detailed knowledge he had, at this time, of either Philoponus' or Benedetti's work. F. Buonamici, who presumably was Galileo's teacher at Pisa, no doubt dealt with Philoponus in his lectures, as he does in his writings. Cf. *De Motu* V, c. 36, p. 504 (Koyré, *Études Galiléennes*, I, 24). See also Introduction, Section III, note 2, above.

heavier, now lighter, according as it is in a lighter or heavier medium.[24] And so, these writers add nothing new when they assume this twofold resistance, since it is merely increased or decreased according to the decrease or increase[25] in the heaviness or density of the medium. But if, on the other hand, they admit that the resistance increases or decreases in the *ratio* in which the weights of the medium vary, their attempts to upset Aristotle's argument will be in vain.

24. Galileo's meaning may be clarified by the memorandum (410.21–26): "Philoponus, Avempace, Avicenna, Saint Thomas, Scotus and others who try to maintain that motion takes place in time [i.e., not instantaneously] in the void, are mistaken when they assert a twofold resistance in the moving body, viz., one accidental and due to the medium, the other intrinsic and due to the body's own weight. These two resistances are clearly one, for the medium, insofar as it is heavier, both offers more resistance and [by that very fact] renders the body lighter."

That is, though one may, by abstracting, analyze the weight of a body in a medium into two factors (weight of the body in a void, and weight of the medium in a void), these factors do not act independently and are not separable in the actual case of a body in a medium.

25. "Decrease or increase" seems to be a slip for "increase or decrease."

285   Chapter [11]

In which the error of Aristotle, in saying that air has weight in its own place, is made clear.

The method that we shall follow in this treatise will be always to make what is said depend on what was said before, and, if possible, never to assume as true that which requires proof. My teachers of mathematics taught me this method. But it is not adhered to sufficiently by certain philosophers who frequently, when they expound the elements of physics, make assumptions that are the same as those handed down in [Aristotle's] books *On the Soul* or those *On the Heaven,* and even in the *Metaphysics.* And not only this, but even in expounding logic itself they continually repeat things that were set forth in the last books of Aristotle. That is, in teaching their pupils the very first subjects, they assume that the pupils know everything, and they pass on to them their teaching, not on the basis of things that the pupils know, but on the basis of what is completely unknown and unheard of. The result is that those who learn in this way never know anything by its causes, but merely have opinions based on belief, that is, because this is what Aristotle said. And few of them inquire whether what Aristotle said is true. For it suffices for them that they will be considered more learned, the more passages of Aristotle they have ready for use. But, leaving this aside and returning to our subject, we must consider whether air and water really have weight in their own proper places. For this is a problem that can be answered with the assumption of only those propositions which we have already set forth.

Aristotle wrote (*De Caelo* 4.30) that not only water but also air has weight in its own proper place, saying that, with the exception of fire, everything, even air itself, has weight in its own region. And he immediately seeks to support his statement about air by evidence, saying that the fact that an inflated bladder weighs more than an uninflated one is evidence the air in the bladder has weight.[1] He repeats the same general proposition in section 39 of the same book, saying that everything that has both weight and lightness has weight in its own place: for he asserts that air and water, in relation to other elements, are sometimes heavy and sometimes light, but are absolutely heavy only in their own proper place.[2] Now some more recent philosophers noted what Aristotle wrote (*De Caelo* 3.28), namely, that air helps both kinds of motion—that, insofar as it is light, it helps upward motion, and insofar as it is heavy, it helps downward motion.[3] They consequently constructed another argument as follows: air, because it carries heavy bodies downward more easily, helps downward motion more than it helps upward motion, because it carries lighter bodies upward with more difficulty. They concluded that air must necessarily be considered heavy in its own place. But it will soon be obvious that this is entirely false. And we shall prove that air and water are neither heavy nor light in their own place.[4] And we shall then prove that the argument of the more recent philosophers leads to a conclusion exactly the opposite of that which they seek to prove, and that they could not have found an argument which was more at variance with their own view.

286

To begin with, it seems entirely inconceivable that air and water should have weight in their own places. To be sure, some portion of water has weight in the place of air, i.e., in the air itself, and indeed moves downward because it has weight. But who will ever conceive of some portion of water sinking in

1. 311b8–10. The view was challenged in antiquity. In fact, Ptolemy obtained the opposite experimental result. Cf. Simplicius, *Comm. in Arist. De Caelo*, pp. 710 f. (Heiberg).
2. Cf. 312b2–19.
3. 301b22–26.
4. Marginal note: "There follows the question whether the absolutely heavy and the absolutely light exist"—an obvious reference to the next chapter (F).

water? For if it does sink, then when it is at the bottom, the place into which it comes has to be vacated by a second portion of water which will have been made to rise to the place which the first portion left. And so this [second] portion of water will be[5] light in its own place. Secondly, if some portion of water has weight in water, suppose, for instance, that this portion is *a*. Now, since the portion of water *a* is heavy in water and moves downward, if we take some other portion of water equal in volume to *a, a* will necessarily be heavier than this second portion of water; thus, water will be heavier than water. But what more absurd result can be conceived?

And to Aristotle's example of the bladder[6] my answer is that if the aperture of the inflated bladder or ball is kept open so that air is retained in the ball, but not compressed by force, the ball will not be any heavier than when not inflated. But if a great deal of air is compressed in it by force, who can doubt that this air will have weight? For this air, being compressed by force, will then be heavier than the free, diffused air. Thus, if a bladder is filled with wool, and then an equal [additional] quantity of wool is inserted by forcible compression, will anyone have any doubts as to whether the bladder will become heavier or not? By similar reasoning, if we consider a portion of air *a* and another portion of air *b,* twice as large as *a,* then in the region of fire, for example, air *b* will be twice as heavy as air *a*. If then air *b* is forcibly compressed, so that its volume becomes equal to the volume of *a,* air *b* will now be, in a sense, another kind of air, heavier than air *a*. What then is so strange if air *b* moves downward in the air of which *a* is part? The reason, then, why the inflated bladder weighs more is clear. For the air which is in it is heavier than the surrounding air, to the extent that it contains more of the same matter in a smaller space. Clearly, then, the argument about the bladder has no force. For, wishing to show that air, free and thin, as its nature is, has weight [in air], Aristotle in his example takes air that is forcibly condensed and compressed in a narrow space.

Now in answer to those who argue that air has weight because it carries heavy bodies down more easily than light bodies up, I say that an argument of that form works in diametric opposition to those who put it forth. Thus, if that medium is to be thought heavy because it easily carries heavy bodies down, air will be heavier than water. For those things that move downward fall

287

5. I.e., "must have been" when it was in the lower position.
6. 311b9–10.

more easily and more swiftly in air than in water. Moreover, it was shown above that heavy bodies that sink in water, sink with a force measured by the difference in weight between their own weight and the weight of a volume of water equal to their volume.

Thus, if there is a heavy body, e.g., *a,* with a weight of 8, and the weight of water *b,* whose volume is equal to the volume of *a,* is 4, the solid *a* will move downward in the water with a speed and facility that may be represented by 4. But then, if the same body moved through a medium lighter than medium *b,* and such that the weight of a volume of this new medium equal to the volume of *b* had a weight of only 3, then *a* would move in the new medium with a speed and facility represented by 5. It is clear, therefore, that the same body *a* moves downward more easily through lighter media than through heavier. It follows, therefore, that a medium must be considered lighter to the extent that heavy bodies move down in it more easily. But those [whom we are refuting] asserted the opposite of this proposition. To whom, then, is it not now perfectly clear that, if the air were still lighter, heavy bodies would move downward through it still more easily? And if this is so, it follows that air is light inasmuch as heavy bodies easily move downward in it.

And reasoning about light bodies in a corresponding manner, we shall conclude that that medium is to be considered heavy, through which light bodies move upward more easily; and that medium light, through which light bodies rise with difficulty. Therefore, both because light bodies move upward in air with some difficulty, and because heavy bodies move downward in air more easily, it follows that air should be *288* considered light rather than heavy. But this is the only conclusion I would draw by reasoning in their fashion. If it is a sound method, let them see for themselves what conclusion may be drawn. But, as far as I am concerned, I would say that in their own places the elements are neither heavy nor light. For if a part of the water were heavy in water, it would sink. But it does not do this. And if it were heavy, how, when we swim under water, would we not feel the weight of so vast an amount of water? To this they would answer: "because the parts of water adhere to the parts below them, just as the bricks of a wall rest on the bricks below; and, they say, that is how it happens that a mouse who lives in a wall does not feel the weight of the stones."[7]

7. Marginal note: "Simplicius De Caelo IV.30" [*Comm. in Arist. De Caelo,* pp. 709–12 (Heiberg)] (F).

But this comparison does not seem to be quite appropriate. For, in the first place, they compare fluid, labile water with a firm, solid wall. Again, an indication that the bricks do not rest on the mouse's back is the fact that, if you take the mouse away, there remains the opening where the mouse was, and the bricks do not slip into it. On the other hand, when a fish or a man is taken from the water, the place where the man was does not remain, but is immediately filled by the water; and this indicates that the water does rest on the fish and men. How, then, will the problem be solved, unless we say that water and air are not heavy in their own regions?

Thus the whole explanation of the problem is as follows. We are said to be weighed down only when some weight rests on us which by its heaviness tends downward, while we must by our force resist its further downward movement; and it is that resistance which we call being weighed down. But it has already been shown that bodies heavier than water, when let down in the water, sink, and are, to be sure, heavy in water but less heavy than in air; and it also has been shown that bodies lighter than water, when forcibly immersed under the water, move upward; and that those which are of the same weight as water move neither up nor down, but remain just where they are placed, provided that they are entirely under water. From this it is clear that if, when we are under water, some body heavier than water, such as a stone, rests upon us, we shall be weighed down, to be sure, but less than if we were in air, because the stone is less heavy in water than in air. But if, when we are in the water, some body lighter than water is fastened to us, not only will we not be weighed down, but we will be buoyed up by it.

This is clear in the case of those who swim with a [hollow] gourd, though under other conditions, when we are in the air we are weighed down by the gourd. And the reason for this is that, when the gourd is immersed in the water, it moves up and lifts up, but in the air it moves down and weighs down. But if, when we are in the water, some body of the same weight as water

289   rests upon us, neither will we be weighed down nor lifted up by it, because such a body will move neither upward nor downward. But no body can be found more nearly equal in weight to water than water itself. It is therefore not strange if water does not move down and weigh down in water. For we have said that to be weighed down means to resist with our strength a body that tends to move downward.

And exactly the same reasoning should be used in discussing air.[8]

This, in my judgment, is the true explanation of the problem, whatever others may say. Therefore, since neither air nor water moves downward or upward in its own region, they should not be called either heavy or light. For heavy bodies, by definition, are those that move downward, and light those that move upward. And when we speak of motion, we must always take account not only of the weight or lightness of the moving body, but also of the weight and lightness of the medium. A heavy body will not move downward, unless it is heavier than the medium through which it must move; nor will a light body rise unless it is lighter than the medium through which it moves. This being so, water will not sink in water, since water is not heavier than water; and since water does not sink, it will not be heavy in water. But it may be asked whether the elements have weight, not as Aristotle considered them, but in and of themselves, simply, absolutely, and not with respect to something else. To this question our answer is that not merely water and earth and air have weight, but even fire, and whatever is lighter than fire, and, in short, everything that has size and matter linked with its being. But since Aristotle holds a contrary view on this question, and posits an absolutely light which nowhere has weight, we think that such an opinion is worthy of examination. And this is what we shall do in the following chapter.

8. I.e., in discussing whether air has weight in air.

Chapter [12]

In which, in opposition to Aristotle, it is concluded that the absolutely light and the absolutely heavy should not be posited; and that even if they existed, they would not be earth and fire, as he believed.

Those who came before Aristotle[1] viewed the heavy and the light only in comparison with less heavy or less light bodies, and, in my opinion, they were perfectly right. But Aristotle, in *De Caelo* Book 4, tries to refute this view of the earlier philosophers

1. In particular, the Atomists and Plato. Buonamici (*De Motu* IV, c. 37, p. 410, as cited by A. Koyré, *Études Galiléennes,* I, 29), discussing the same point and not limiting himself to pre-Aristotelians, mentions Timaeus, Strato of Lampsacus, and Epicurus.

and to prove his own, which is opposed to it. But since
290   we are going to follow the opinion of the earlier
philosophers on this point, we shall examine both
Aristotle's refutations and his own proofs, proving what he
sought to refute, and refuting what he sought to prove. And we
shall carry this out, after we have expounded Aristotle's own
view.

In the first place, then, Aristotle declares, by way of definition,
that he calls the absolutely heaviest that which lies below everything else and always moves toward the center [of the universe];
and he calls the [absolutely] lightest that which rises above
everything else and always moves up, and never down. This he
writes in *De Caelo* 4.26 and 31.[2] He then declares that the [abso-
lutely] heaviest is earth, and the lightest is fire (section 32,[3] and
other passages). Then, in opposition to those who assert that
there is some heaviness in fire, he argues as follows: "If fire has
some heaviness, it will remain below something; but this is not
observed. Therefore [etc.]."[4] But this argument is not conclusive.
For, in order that one thing should be above another, it is sufficient for it to be less heavy than that above which it must be. It
is not necessary that it be entirely without weight. Thus, for wood
to float on water it is not necessarily required that the wood be
entirely without weight, but it is enough that it be less heavy
than water. And so, by similar reasoning, for fire to be above air
it is enough that it be less heavy than air; it is not necessary that
it be entirely without weight. It is clear, therefore, that this argument of Aristotle does not lead to a necessary conclusion.

Aristotle also argues as follows: "If fire has some weight, it
follows that a large amount of fire will be heavier than a small
amount; hence a large amount of fire will rise in air more slowly
than will a small amount. Similarly, if earth has any lightness, a
large amount of earth, because it will have more lightness, will
fall more slowly than a small amount. But experience shows the
opposite. For we see that a large amount of fire rises more swiftly
than a small amount, just as a large amount of earth falls more
swiftly. This, then, is evidence that there is only lightness in fire;
and since there is more lightness in a great deal of fire, it rises
more swiftly."[5] This, too, is an invalid argument. In the first
place, it goes beyond the proper bounds. For the conclusion in the

2. 308a29–31 (cf. 311a16–18); 311b13–16.
3. 311b20–24.
4. 311b25–27.
5. Cf. 308b16–27.

291
following is invalid: "If fire, considered in and of itself, has weight, a great deal of fire will be heavier in air than will a small amount." For fire has no weight at all in air. Instead, the argument should be framed as follows: "Fire, considered in and of itself, has weight. Therefore, where fire has weight, a great deal of fire will have a large weight; and where fire has lightness, as in air, a large amount of fire will have much lightness, and a small amount will have little lightness." The fallacy in Aristotle's argument is therefore clear.

Secondly, he is mistaken when he asserts that a great deal of fire rises more swiftly than a small amount, or that a great deal of earth falls more swiftly than a small amount. We have shown this above.[6]

Thirdly, he argues as follows: "If fire has weight, a great deal of fire will be heavier than a small amount of air." And he asserts that such a result would be the greatest absurdity, as if we were to say: "If earth has some lightness, there will be a portion of earth lighter than a portion of water." This result he declares to be false because we see that any portion whatever of earth sinks in water and any portion whatever of fire rises in air. Now this argument of Aristotle is even weaker than all the others. For who is so stupid as not to believe that a great deal of water is heavier than a small amount of earth, a great deal of air than a small amount of water, and a great deal of fire than a small amount of air? And this is in no way impugned by Aristotle's statement that we see earth sink in water. For when he says this, he is no longer self-consistent. That is, when we say that water has weight, we do not say that it has weight in its own region: for there, as we have proved, it has neither weight nor lightness. But we do say that a great deal of water is heavier than a small amount of earth in the place where water too has weight, e.g., in air. For if Aristotle's method of reasoning were valid, I could also conclude that a little piece of lead is heavier than the largest beam of wood, because lead sinks in water and wood does not. But the fact is that a little piece of lead is heavier than the wooden beam in a place where the beam has no weight. And if we want to talk about the weight of the beam, we must assume that the beam is in a place where it has weight.

Similarly, when he says, "Any portion whatever of water falls in air; hence any amount whatever of air is lighter than the portion of water," this will be true in a place where air has no

6. See 262–66.

weight, but water does. But this will have nothing to do with absolute weight, the subject we are now discussing. For if we assume a large quantity of air in a place where air too has weight, e.g., in fire or in a void, certainly that air in that place will be heavier than a small amount of water. But the conclusion, "Therefore it will fall more swiftly," would not fol-

292   low. For one who drew such a conclusion would show that he did not understand how slowness and speed of motion come about. Thus it will not be valid to argue: "A bag filled with tow is heavier in air than a small piece of lead; therefore it will fall more swiftly in air." For even a fool would not say this, nor would anyone who understood what we said above. The correct way to reason about fire is as follows: "A great deal of fire will be heavier than a small amount of air—not in air, where fire has no weight, but in some other place where fire, too, has weight, as it would in a void or in a medium lighter than fire."

Heavens! At this point I am weary and ashamed of having to use so many words to refute such childish arguments and such inept attempts at subtleties as those which Aristotle crams into the whole of Book 4 of *De Caelo,* as he argues against the older philosophers. For his arguments have no force, no learning, no elegance or attractiveness, and anyone who has understood what was said above will recognize their fallacies. Thus, when Aristotle says, "we see that earth is below, and fire above, everything else," he must have had the eyes of Lynceus if he could see whether or not there is anything in the bowels of the earth heavier than earth and whether there is any lighter body above fire. But without the eyes of Lynceus a blind man can see that there are many things heavier than earth,[7] e.g., all the metals upon which, when they are in liquid form, earth floats, as it does upon so-called quicksilver. Not only is earth lighter than quicksilver; it is more than ten times as light. How, then, can the metals receive their heaviness from earth, if they are far heavier than earth? And if they consisted of earth, water, air, and fire, would they not have to be far lighter than earth alone? Clearly, then, there are many things heavier than earth. Therefore Aristotle argues inconclusively when he says: "There are two contrary places, the center and the extremity"—he takes as extremity the lunar sphere[8]—"and it is

7. Galileo is here identifying Aristotle's element "earth" with the soil of the ground.

8. I.e., "the concave surface of the [sphere of the] moon." See ch. 8, note 4. The phrase is equivalent to the "region of the moon," i.e., of the moon's orbit.

To each of the terrestrial elements in the Aristotelian system corresponds a

therefore necessary that what is in those places be opposites. This
will not be the case unless earth is assumed to be free from all
lightness and fire free from all heaviness."[9] But even if the argument did involve a necessary conclusion, the fact is that the regions of water and of air are opposite to the center in precisely
the same way as is the region of the moon; and yet, what is contained beneath the region of air is not devoid of all weight.[10]

Again, Aristotle writes about the lightness of fire, that if air is
removed from under it fire will not move downward, as will air
when water is removed.[11] But this requires proof; and Aristotle
failed to give that proof, unless one were to consider as proof his
statement: "Just as earth does not rise in the cupping glasses of
physicians because it is absolutely heavy, so fire will not move
downward because it is absolutely light."[12] But the
293   analogy is invalid, for earth does not rise, not because
          it is absolutely heavy, but because it is not fluid. In fact,
neither would wood rise, though it is lighter than water, which
does rise. On the other hand, mercury, though it is heavier than
earth, would rise because it is fluid. So too fire would move downward, because it is not solid but fluid.[13]

But suppose that the elements are transmuted into one another,
as Aristotle himself holds.[14] Then, I ask you, when fire is made
from heavy air, what happens to that heaviness of the air? Is it
perhaps destroyed? But if it is destroyed, where does the heaviness come from when, in its turn, earth is made from fire? Does
the heaviness, which is something, perhaps come from nonheaviness, which is nothing?

Furthermore, if fire is without any weight whatever, it will

---

sphere having as center the center of the universe, in the order, earth, water, air,
and fire, proceeding from the center. The region of air, for example, would be
the region above the surface of the sphere of water and below the surface of the
sphere of air; and the phrase *concavum aeris,* "the concave surface of [the sphere]
of air," the upper extremity of the region of air, might stand for "region of air."
I have so translated it in this paragraph.

9. Cf. 311b27–312a10.

10. The words of this sentence after the *if* clause are underlined in the manuscript and there is the marginal note: "Plato writes the same thing in the
Timaeus" (F). [Cf. *Timaeus* 62–63.]

11. Cf. 312b5–19.

12. 312b13–16.

13. Marginal addition: "Heavy and light are defined in terms of upward and
downward. If, then, there is an absolute heavy and an absolute light, there will
be an absolute down and an absolute up. But the absolute down and the absolute
up are not places. For one is an indivisible point and the other a pure surface"
(F).

14. Cf. *De Generatione et Corruptione.* See also Memorandum 409.4–7.

therefore be without any density whatever. For density is a consequence of weight. But what is without any density is a void. Hence fire is a void. But what could be more absurd? And, finally, how can anyone ever conceive of fire as a substance in which weight is not linked with extension? Surely this appears quite contrary to reason.

And when we say that earth is the heaviest of all substances because it lies below all the others, we are compelled, whether we like it or not, to say that earth is heaviest in comparison with the others, by the very fact of lying below all others. For lying below all other substances and being heaviest of all substances are one and the same. And this conclusion is clear. For if the heaviest is that which lies below everything else, then if everything else is removed, it can no longer be called heaviest, since it no longer lies below anything. It is therefore called heaviest in comparison with the less heavy substances below which it lies. And a similar argument applies to the lightness of fire. We conclude, therefore, that it is impossible for anything to be called heaviest, except in comparison with other things which are less heavy, since the heaviest cannot be defined or conceived except insofar as it lies below the less heavy; and, in the same way, that it is impossible for anything to be called lightest, except in comparison with things which are less light and above which it rises; and that the lightest substance is not that which lacks all weight—for this is a void, not some substance—but that which is less heavy than all the other substances that have weight.

Now I would not say that there is not found in the nature of things some substance which is heavier than all others, and some substance which is lighter, that is to say, less heavy, than all others. I merely make these two denials—first, that these can be considered the heaviest and lightest substances absolutely, without comparison with other substances; and, secondly, that these substances are earth and fire. For many things are heavier than earth, things which we actually see. And *294* there might also be some things lighter than fire, perhaps some vapors[15] which rise above fire; but we cannot confidently assert this because we have never been above fire.

But even if the lightest substance is fire, still it is not entirely without weight, for that is a property of the void. Therefore, fire, too, will move downward if air is removed from under it, that is, if a void or some other medium lighter than fire is left under it.

---

15. Galileo is probably thinking of comets. So in the reworking (360.28), translated in Appendix I.

For all things move downward provided they are heavier than the medium through which they are to move, as was shown above; and there is nothing contradictory about motion taking place in a void, as was also shown.[16] But as a matter of fact, the reason that fire does not move downward is not that fire has no weight, but that air, through which the fire would have to move, is heavier than fire. So too, the reason that air does not move downward is that it would have to move through water, and water, being heavier than air, does not permit this. Yet we must not say that air, just because it does not move downward, is entirely without weight.

16. Ch. 10.

Chapter [13]

In which, in opposition to Aristotle and Themistius, it is proved that only in a void can differences of weights and motions be exactly determined.

Themistius, following Aristotle's view, writes in his discussion of the void (on *Physics* 4.74):[1] "Since, then, the void gives way evenly, and yet does not give way at all (for since the void is nothing, to hold that the void gives way is the mark of an over-acute mind), the result is that differences between heavy bodies and light bodies, i.e., between their motions, are removed; and, as a consequence, the speed of all bodies moving [naturally] becomes equal and without difference." How false this is will become clear presently when we have shown that only in a void can the true differences of weights and motions be determined, and that these cannot be discovered in any plenum.

To begin with, just as among philosophers diverse opinions on the same subject provide strong evidence that none of them has discovered the truth—for if the truth had once been found by any of them, immediately and without any controversy, its nature being what it is, it would have allowed itself to be inspected and understood by all; so, in the same way, the diverse ratios between the weights of the same bodies in different media are strong proof that the true, natural weights cannot be determined in connection with any medium. For the heavier a medium is, the greater is the interval [as a ratio] between the weights of solids.

295　　　　That this may more easily be understood now, recall the demonstrations that were made above. It was

1. Pp. 133.32–133.2, ed. H. Schenkl (Berlin, 1900). The same quotation is found in a memorandum (412.3–7).

proved, for example, that a solid weighs less in water than in air by a weight (in air) of a volume of water equal to the volume of the solid. Thus, suppose there are two solids *a* and *b,* that the weight of *a* in air is 8, and of *b* 6, that their volumes are equal, and that the weight (in air) of an equal volume of water *c* is 3. It is clear from what has just been said that the weight in water of *a* is 5, and of *b* 3. The interval [as a ratio], then, between the weights of *a* and *b* in water will be greater; thus the interval [as a ratio] of 5 to 3 is greater than that of 8 to 6. If, now, there is some medium heavier than water, whose weight is, say, 5, the weight of *a* in it will be 3 and of *b* 1. Thus it is clear that as the media become heavier, the interval [as a ratio] between the weights is always greater. For the ratio of weight *a* to weight *b* in air is 4 to 3, in water 5 to 3, and in the third medium 3 to 1.[2]

But who will say that the true weights of the solids are to be found in this rather than in that medium? Surely no one. But at least it will be truer to say that in none of these media are the exact weights obtained. For since in every medium the weights of heavy bodies are diminished by the weight of a portion of that medium equal in size to the solid, it is clear that the whole and undiminished weights of solids will be obtained only in that medium whose weight is zero. And such a medium can only be the void. But in other media heavy bodies weigh and bear down only to the extent that they are heavier than those media. For if they were only just as heavy as some medium, they would have no weight in that medium. And since, similarly, the weight of solids in the void is measured by the amount by which with their own heaviness they overbalance the weight of the void, and since they overbalance [the weight of the void] to the extent of their own weight (for the weight of the void is zero), it is a necessary consequence that only in the void can the true weights of heavy bodies be obtained. And therefore only in the void will the [true] intervals [i.e., ratios] between such weights be present.

Similar considerations hold for the velocities of motions and the ratios of these velocities. For who will say that the [true] velocities can be found in nonvacuous media, if a body has one velocity in this medium, another in that one, still another in another medium, and even a velocity of zero in still another medium, e.g., the velocity of wood in water; and, similarly, if there is one ratio of velocities in air, another in water, one ratio in a heavier medium, and another in a lighter medium, as anyone

---

2. And, in general, if $a > b > c > d > 0$, then $(a - c) / (b - c) > (a - d) / (b - d)$.

can easily find from what has been written above? And finally, since the velocities of bodies depend on their weights in the medium in which they move, and since, as a consequence, the ratios of these velocities depend on the ratios of these weights, and since the [true] weights are not obtained except in the void, we may assert beyond any doubt that only in the void can the true and natural ratios of velocities occur.

296

Chapter [14]

Containing a discussion of the ratios of the [speeds of the] motions of the same body moving over various inclined planes.

The problem we are now going to discuss has not been taken up by any philosophers, so far as I know.[1] Yet, since it has to do with motion, it seems to be a necessary subject for examination by those who claim to give a treatment of motion that is not incomplete. And it is a problem no less necessary than neat and elegant. The problem is why the same heavy body, moving downward in natural motion over various planes inclined to the plane of the horizon, moves more readily and swiftly on those planes that make angles nearer a right angle with the horizon; and, in addition, the problem calls for the ratio [of the speeds] of the motions that take place at the various inclinations. The solution of this problem, when first I had tried to investigate it, seemed to require explanations that were by no means simple. But while I was examining it more carefully, and was trying to analyze its solution into its basic principles, I finally discovered that the solution of this problem, as of others which at first glance seem very difficult, depended on known and obvious principles of nature. We shall begin now by setting forth these ideas, since they are needed for our explanation of the problem.

And first, so that everything may be better understood, let us explain the problem by an example. Let there be a line *ab* directed toward the center of the universe and thus perpendicular to a plane parallel to the horizon. And let line *bc* lie in that plane parallel to the horizon. Now from point *b* let any number of lines be drawn making acute angles with line *bc*, e.g., lines *bd* and *be*. The problem, then, is why a body moving down descends most quickly on line *ab;* and on line *bd* more quickly than on

---

1. On Galilean and pre-Galilean discussions of the inclined plane see the introduction and notes to the *Mechanics*, below. Even on the specific question of the ratio of speeds Galileo can hardly claim priority.

297 *be*, but more slowly than on *ba;* and on *be* more slowly than on *bd*. We must find, furthermore, how much faster the body descends on *ba* than on *bd*, and how much faster on *bd* than on *be*.

Now to be able to answer these questions, we must first take into consideration what we noted above,[2] namely (as is quite clear), that a heavy body tends to move downward with as much force as is necessary to lift it up; i.e., it tends to move downward with the same force with which it resists rising. If, then, we can find with how much less force the heavy body can be drawn up on line *bd* than on line *ba*, we will then have found with how much greater force the same heavy body descends on line *ab* than on line *bd*. And, similarly, if we can find how much greater force is needed to draw the body upward on line *bd* than on *be*, we will then have found with how much greater force the body will descend on *bd* than on *be*. But we shall know how much less force is required to draw the body upward on *bd* than on *be* as soon as we find out how much greater will be the weight of that body on the [inclined] plane along *bd*[3] than on the plane along *be*.

Let us proceed then to investigate this weight. Consider a balance *cd*, with center *a*, having at point *c* a weight equal to another weight at point *d*. Now, if we suppose that line *ad* moves toward *b*, pivoting about the fixed point *a*, then the descent of the body, at the initial point *d*, will be as if on line *ef*.[4] Therefore, the descent of the body on line *ef* will be a consequence of the weight of the body at point *d*. Again, when the body is at *s*, its descent at the initial point *s* will be as if on line *gh;* and hence the motion of the body on *gh* will be a consequence of the weight that the body has at point *s*. And again, at the time when the body is at point *r*, its descent at the initial point *r* will be as if on line *tn;* hence the body will move on line *tn* in consequence of the weight that it has at point *r*.

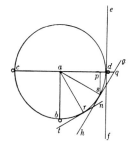

298 If, then, we can show that the body is less heavy at point *s* than at point *d*, clearly its motion on line *gh* will be slower than on *ef*. And if, again, we can show that the body at *r* is still less heavy than at point *s*, clearly the motion on line *nt* will be slower than on *gh*. Now it is clear that the body exerts less force at point *r* than at point *s*, and less at *s* than at *d*. For the weight at point *d* just balances the weight at point *c*,

2. Ch. 9.
3. I.e., the plane containing *bd* and perpendicular to the plane of *ab* and *bc*.
4. I.e., tangent to the circle at *d*. So *gh* is tangent at *s* and *tn* at *r*.

since the distances *ca* and *ad* are equal. But the weight at point *s* does not balance that at *c*. For if a line is drawn from point *s* perpendicular to *cd,* the weight at *s,* as compared with the weight at *c,* is as if it were suspended from *p.* But a weight at *p* exerts less force than the [equal] weight at *c,* since the distance *pa* is less than distance *ac.* Similarly, a weight at *r* exerts less force than an [equal] weight at *s:* this will likewise become clear if we draw a perpendicular from *r* to *ad,* for this perpendicular will intersect *ad* between points *a* and *p.* It is obvious, then, that the body will descend on line *ef* with greater force than on line *gh,* and on *gh* with greater force than on *nt.*

But with *how much* greater force it moves on *ef* than on *gh* will be made clear as follows, viz., by extending line *ad* beyond the circle, to intersect line *gh* at point *q.* Now since the body descends on line *ef* more readily than on *gh* in the same ratio as the body is heavier at point *d* than at point *s,* and since it is heavier at *d* than at *s* in proportion as line *da* is longer than *ap,* it follows that the body will descend on line *ef* more readily than on *gh* in proportion as line *da* is longer than *pa.* Therefore the speed on *ef* will bear to the speed on *gh* the same ratio as line *da* to line *pa.* And as *da* is to *pa,* so is *qs* to *sp,* i.e., the length of the oblique descent to the length of the vertical drop. And it is clear that the same weight can be drawn up an inclined plane with less force than vertically, in proportion as the vertical ascent is smaller than the oblique.[5] Consequently, the same heavy body will descend vertically with greater force than on an inclined plane in proportion as the length of the descent on the incline is greater than the vertical fall.

But this proof must be understood on the assumption that there is no accidental resistance (occasioned by roughness of the moving body or of the inclined plane, or by the shape of the body). We must assume that the plane is, so to speak, incorporeal or, at least, that it is very carefully smoothed and perfectly hard, so that, as the body exerts its pressure on the plane, it may not cause a bending of the plane and somehow come to rest on it, as in a trap. And the moving body must be [assumed to be] perfectly smooth, of a shape that does not resist motion, e.g., a perfectly spherical shape, and of the hardest material or else a fluid like water. If everything is arranged in this way, then any body on a plane parallel to the horizon will be moved by the very smallest force, indeed, by a force less than any

299

5. $\dfrac{\text{force required to overcome weight on incline}}{\text{force required to overcome weight vertically}} = \dfrac{\text{vertical height}}{\text{oblique distance}}$

given force. Since this seems quite hard to believe, it will be proved by the following demonstration.

Let there be a circle with center *a*, and a balance *bc* that can turn about its center *a* and is parallel to the horizon; and let a perpendicular *ad* be drawn from the center *a* in the direction of the center of the universe. Now suppose that some weight hangs from point *d*. Clearly the weight at *d* as it moves toward *c* must rise. I say, then, that any force whatever exerted upon point *b* can move the weight at *d*, and does necessarily move it. For consider any weight, however small, hanging from point *b*. And as the weight at *d* is to the weight at *b*, so let line *ba* be to another line. Let the distance *ae* be equal to that other line. Now if [the weight at] *d* should hang from point *e*, it will then be in equilibrium with the weight at *b*; neither weight will be moved by the other, nor will the balance turn. But the weight at *d*, suspended as it is from *a*, is lighter than if it hangs from *e*, since it is suspended not merely from a point nearer the center, but from the center itself. Hence the weight at *d*, suspended from *a*, must be moved by the weight at *b*,[6] and the balance inclines [downward] on the side of *b* and *d* moves up. Therefore, if with any force [however small] any weight [however large] at *d* is not merely moved but even raised, why is it strange that that same weight at *d* should be moved, on a plane that does not slope up, by the same or an even smaller force than the force at *b*?

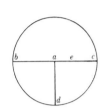

But there is more. A body subject to no external resistance on a plane sloping no matter how little below the horizon will move down [the plane] in natural motion, without the application of any external force. This can be seen in the case of water. And the same body on a plane sloping upward, no matter how little, above the horizon, does not move up [the plane] except by force. And so the conclusion remains that on the horizontal plane itself the motion of the body is neither natural nor forced.[7] But if its motion is not forced motion, then it can be made to move by the smallest of all possible forces.

And we can also in another way demonstrate this proposition, that a body subject to no external resistance can be moved on a plane which slopes neither up nor down by a force smaller than any given force whatever. For the proof of this proposition we make the following assumption: any heavy body can be moved on a plane parallel to the horizon

300

6. *ad* is considered to be rigidly attached to *bc*.

7. This conclusion represents a step toward the elimination of the dichotomy of natural and forced motion, a step ultimately toward the inertial concept.

by a smaller force than up along a plane sloping above the horizon. Let line *ab* represent a plane parallel to the horizon, and let *bc* be perpendicular to *ab;* let *e* be a spherical body, and *f* any force whatever. I say that sphere *e*, if subject to no external and accidental resistance, can be moved on plane *ab* by a force smaller than *f*. Let *n* represent the force which can lift weight *e;* and let line *ad* be to line *db* as force *n* is to force *f*. Now from what has already been proved,[8] sphere *e* will be able to be drawn up plane *ad* by force *f*. Therefore sphere *e* will be moved on plane *ab* by a force smaller than *f*. Which was to be proved.[9]

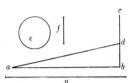

Now I am not unaware that someone at this point may object that for the purpose of these proofs I am assuming as true the proposition that weights suspended from a balance make right angles with the balance—a proposition that is false, since the weights, directed as they are to the center [of the universe], are convergent. To such objectors I would answer that I cover myself with the protecting wings of the superhuman Archimedes, whose name I never mention without a feeling of awe. For he made this same assumption in his *Quadrature of the Parabola*.[10] And he did so perhaps to show that he was so far ahead of others that he could draw true conclusions even from false assumptions. Yet we must not suppose, in a moment of doubt, that his conclusion is false, since he had earlier demonstrated the same conclusion by another geometric proof. Therefore we must say either that the suspended weights actually do make right angles with the balance, or else that it is of no importance that they make right angles, but that it is enough that the angles are equal. The latter will perhaps be sounder, unless we wish to say rather that this is a case of geometric license, as when Archimedes also assumes that

8. See 298.

9. Marginal addition: "From this it follows that mixed motion does not exist." [After the phrase "mixed motion" the author had written and then deleted "except circular."] "For since the forced motion of heavy bodies is away from the center, and their natural motion toward the center, a motion which is partly upward and partly downward cannot be compounded from these two; unless perhaps we should say that such a mixed motion is that which takes place on the circumference of a circle around the center of the universe. But such motion will be better described as 'neutral' than as 'mixed.' For 'mixed' partakes of both [natural and forced], 'neutral' of neither" (F). (On the subject of mixed motion, see the dialogue version 373.5 ff.)

10. Not in so many words. But the weights suspended from the ends of a horizontal lever in equilibrium are assumed to hang perpendicularly to the lever. Benedetti had only a few years before (*Diversarum speculationum . . . liber*, pp. 148–51) criticized the same assumption in Jordanus and Tartaglia. Ubaldi, too, had discussed the same matter in his *Mechanics* (1577) and it was widely debated in the following century.

surfaces have weight,[11] and that one surface is heavier than another, whereas, in point of fact, they are entirely without weight.

301   And our demonstrations, as we also said above, must be understood of bodies free from all external resistance. But since it is perhaps impossible to find such bodies in the realm of matter, one who performs an experiment on the subject should not be surprised if the experiment fails, that is, if a large sphere, even though it is on a horizontal plane, cannot be moved with a minimal force. For in addition to the causes already mentioned,[12] there is also this one—that a plane cannot actually be parallel to the horizon,[13] since the surface of the earth is spherical, and a plane cannot be parallel to such a surface. Hence, since [in the aforesaid experiment] the plane touches the sphere in only one point, if we move away from that point, we shall have to be moving up. There is good reason, therefore, why it will not be possible to move the sphere from that point with an arbitrarily minimal force.

From what has been proved, it will be easy to obtain the solution of certain problems like the following. First, given two inclined planes whose descent, measured perpendicularly, is the same, to find the ratio of the speeds of the same body moving on them. Let the perpendicular distance down be *ab* and the plane of the horizon *bd,* and let the oblique paths down be *ac* and *ad.* Now the question is what ratio the speed on *ca* bears to the speed on *ad.* And since line *da* is to line *ab* as the slowness on *ad* is to the slowness on *ab,* as has been shown above;[14] and since the slowness on *ab* is to the slowness on *ac* as line *ab* is to line *ac,* it follows, *ex aequali,*[15] that line *da* will be to line *ac* as the slowness on *ad* is to the slowness on *ac.* And therefore line *da* will be to line *ac* also as the speed on *ac* is to the speed on *ad.* It is clear, then, that the speeds of the same body moving on different inclinations are to each other inversely as the lengths of the oblique paths, if these entail equal vertical descents.[16]

11. In speaking of centers of gravity of triangles, etc.

12. See above, 298.

13. What Galileo means is that no plane but only a spherical surface can have all its points equally distant from the center of the universe.

14. See above, 298. The ratio of the slownesses on *ad* and *ab* is the same as the ratio of the speeds on *ab* and *ad.*

15. I.e., by multiplying the respective members of the two equations.

16. We may understand Galileo's theorem as stating that the times required for descent are directly proportional to the lengths of the oblique paths, or, alternately, that the speeds attained *in fixed intervals of time* are inversely proportional to the length of the oblique paths. In that limited sense the theorem would be sound. But there is no indication that this is what Galileo had in mind, and,

Furthermore, we are able to find inclined planes such that the speeds on them of a given body will be in a given ratio. For let the given ratio be that which line *e* bears to *f*. And let *da* and *ac* in the preceding diagram be constructed in the ratio of *e* to *f*. The problem will thus be solved.[17]

Other similar problems can be solved, e.g., given two bodies of different material but equal size, to construct a plane so inclined, that the body which, in a vertical fall, moves more swiftly than the other will descend on this plane with the same speed with which the other would fall vertically.[18] But since these and similar problems and solutions can easily be discovered by

302   those who understand what was said above, we discreetly omit them. We note only this, that, just as was said before of vertical motion, so also in the case of the motions on planes, it happens that the ratios we have set down are not observed. This happens not only for the reasons just now given,[19] but also—and this is accidental—because a lighter body descends more quickly than a heavier one at the beginning of its motion. How this comes about we shall make clear at the proper place:[20] for this question depends on the question why natural motion is accelerated. But, as we have often said, these proofs of ours assume that there are no external interferences with the motion resulting from the shape of the body, or roughness of the plane or the body, or motion of the medium in the opposite or in the same direction [as that of the body], or the force of an external mover that promotes or retards the motion, and the like. Rules cannot be given for these accidental factors since they can occur in countless ways. Similar considerations apply to the discussion of upward motion.

Let this suffice for the subject of motion on inclined planes. It remains for us to say something in the next chapter about circular motion, investigating, to begin with, whether it has a ratio to rectilinear motion or not, and whether it is forced motion or natural motion.

---

in any case, the inadequacy of Galileo's doctrine of the velocity of free fall prevents any fruitful generalization and extension of these results.

17. Here, again, Galileo would be on sound ground only if "speed" is interpreted in the way indicated in the preceding note.

18. If the problem be interpreted as requiring that the vertical and oblique falls involve the same vertical distance and end simultaneously, Galileo's solution would be to make the ratio of the oblique and vertical paths equal to the given ratio of the speeds of the vertical falls. But insofar as this latter ratio is ultimately based on a delusion, the problem itself is unreal.

19. 298, above.

20. Ch. 22, below.

Chapter [15]

In which, in opposition to Aristotle, the conclusion is reached that rectilinear and circular motions have a ratio[1] to each other.

That Aristotle was little versed in geometry is clear in many passages of his philosophical work, but particularly in the passage where he asserts[2] that circular motion does not have any ratio to rectilinear motion because, as he says, a straight line is not in any ratio to or comparable to a curve. But this falsehood (for it is unworthy of the term "opinion") shows that Aristotle was ignorant not only of the profound and more abstruse discoveries of geometry, but even of the most elementary principles of this science. For how could he say that rectilinear and circular motion have no ratio if, for quantities to have a ratio to each other, it is sufficient that we be able to add the smaller to itself so many times that it will exceed the larger? Or would you say
303   that the chord of an arc, which is less than the arc, will not, if added to itself often enough, exceed the length of the arc? But if it will exceed it, why does Aristotle say that the arc and chord do not have a ratio?

Yet there have not been lacking those who try to defend Aristotle by saying that he meant merely this, that the curved and the straight are not comparable. But those people are far more inept in geometry even than Aristotle. For, in trying to show that he did not err, they attribute to him an error which is far more serious than that from which they try to absolve him. In the first place, where in geometry did they find mention made of ratio or lack of ratio of the curved and the straight, when a ratio is not found except where there is greater and lesser, i.e., where there is quantity? But who would ever call the curved and the straight quantities? But could Aristotle ever have thought of any greater piece of foolishness than to say that the curved and the straight are not in a ratio to each other or comparable? For this would be like saying that a triangle and a square are not comparable because the triangle has only three angles, and the square four. But what is the point of this, when Aristotle did not mean what they have in mind? For this is what he says (*Physics* 7.24): "If a straight line and a curve are comparable, it turns out that

1. Galileo used this word (*proportio*) in what follows virtually in the sense of "quantitative relation." It would not exclude the irrational and the incommensurable.
2. *Physics* 248a19–b6.

there is a straight line equal to a circle. But these are not comparable."[3]

Those are his words. But, to refute these [other writers] so that they have no escape, I shall argue in the following way. Surely they will not deny that a plane surface has a ratio to some part of itself. But if that is so, I already have achieved my purpose. For a circle inscribed in a square is some part of that square; hence the square has some ratio to the circle. But the square is to the inscribed circle as the perimeter of the square is to the circumference of the circle. Therefore the perimeter of the square, which consists of straight lines, has a ratio to the curved circumference of the circle. But why do I go further? Aristotle is so rash as to say: "There is no straight line equal to the circumference of a circle."[4] That this is false is proved by the divine Archimedes in his work *On Spirals,* proposition [20], where a straight line is found equal to the circumference of the circle around the spiral of first revolution.[5] And one should not say: "Aristotle was unaware of this, for Archimedes comes much later than Aristotle." For if Aristotle was unaware of the solution of the problem of finding a straight line equal to a curved line, he was
304 also unaware of any proof that no straight line existed equal to a curved line. Therefore, he should not have made the rash assertion that such a straight line did not exist.

Furthermore, who is so blind as not to see that, if there are two equal straight lines, one of which is then bent into a curve, that curve will be equal to the straight line? Or if a circle moves over a straight line, who will doubt that in one revolution it traverses a straight line equal to its circumference? Let us then have no doubts that there exists a rectilinear motion equal to a given curvilinear motion, and also rectilinear motion bearing to curvilinear motion any given ratio.

3. 248b4–6. Galileo's point is that Aristotle failed to see that the lines have a quantitative relation even if they are qualitatively different. Cf. Benedetti, *Diversarum speculationum . . . liber,* p. 194.

4. Cf. 248a19–b6.

5. In the spiral of Archimedes the subtangent at the end of the first revolution is equal to the circumference of the circle with radius equal to radius vector of the spiral at the end of that revolution.

Chapter [16]

On the question whether circular motion is natural or forced.

In beginning our discussion of circular motion we shall first subdivide it as follows. Circular motion takes place either about the center of the universe or about another center. Let us now see whether that motion which takes place about the center of the universe is forced motion or not, e.g., if there were a marble sphere at the center of the universe, its center being the same as the center of the universe. We shall have the answer to this question if we make clear what is natural motion and what is forced motion.

Now we have natural motion when bodies, as they move, approach their natural places, and forced motion when the bodies that move recede from their natural place. This being so, it is clear that the sphere rotating about the center of the universe moves with a motion that is neither natural nor forced. For the sphere is a heavy body, and the place of heavy bodies is the center, and the motion of heavy bodies is in accordance with [the motion of] their center of gravity.[1] In view of this, if the center of gravity of the sphere were at the center of the universe, where it would remain at rest while the sphere rotated, clearly the sphere would be moving neither naturally nor by force, since it would neither be approaching nor receding from its natural place. In this it must be noted that if the sphere consisted of homogeneous parts so that its centers of gravity and of magnitude[2] were the same, then its center would not be different from the center of the universe. But if it consisted of heterogeneous parts, so that its center of gravity was different from its center of magnitude, then its center of gravity would be the same as the center of the universe and its center of magnitude different. But, in any case, so long as the center of gravity was the same as the center of the universe,

305   the sphere at the center of the universe would rotate neither naturally nor by force. For the motion of everything that moves is in accordance with [the motion of] its center of gravity. And if the center of gravity is not different from the center of the universe, a sphere rotating about its center of gravity will move neither naturally nor by force.

---

1. I.e., such a body moves as if all its weight were concentrated in its center of gravity, and its motion may be described in terms of the motion of its center of gravity.

2. The center of magnitude is the geometric center.

But two questions arise at this point: first, whether a sphere of heterogeneous parts whose center of magnitude was at the center of the universe, but whose center of gravity did not coincide with the center of the universe, whether, I say, such a sphere would move by force or not; secondly, if at the center of the universe there were a sphere that rotated neither naturally nor by force, the question is asked whether, after receiving a start of motion from an external mover, it would move perpetually or not. For if its motion is not contrary to nature, it seems that it should move perpetually; but if its motion is not according to nature, it seems that it should finally come to rest.

Returning, then, to the first question, we say that it is contrary to nature and due to force that a sphere of heterogeneous parts, whose center of gravity does not coincide with its center of magnitude, remains at rest in such a way that its center of magnitude is at the center of the universe and its center of gravity at another point. But for it to move would not be contrary to nature and due to force. Thus, for example, suppose there is a sphere whose center of magnitude is *a*, which coincides with the center of the universe. And suppose the sphere is heterogeneous, being made, let us say, of wood, but having at the part labelled *o* a piece of lead. The center of gravity of such a sphere would be between *a* and *o*, say at *c*. Clearly, the sphere will not be held in this place [i.e., with *a* at the center of the universe] except by force. For since heavy bodies tend toward the center [of the universe] and move toward it in accordance with [the motion of] their center of gravity, the center of gravity *c* of the sphere would move naturally toward *a*, the center of the universe. Hence *c* will be kept outside this center only by force. But rotation of the sphere about[3] the center of the universe would not be by force, for in such a rotation the center of gravity would describe a circle about the center of the universe, neither approaching it nor receding from it. This being the case, it will rotate neither naturally nor by force. For it would be moving naturally, as we said above, only when it [i.e., the center of gravity of the sphere] approached the center of the universe, and by force, only if, in its motion, it receded from that center.

This makes clear the error of those who say that if a single star were added to the heavens, the motion of the heavens would either cease or become slower. Actually, neither of these things would happen. For since, in their view,

306

---

3. Reading *circa* or *super* (for *extra*), 305.28. The slip may be due to *extra* in the preceding line.

too, the rotation of the heavens takes place about the center of the universe, the adding of a star or the further addition of any other heavy weight will neither help along nor retard the motion. The reason is that such a weight, in such rotation, neither increases nor decreases its nearness to or distance from the center, toward which it would tend to move by reason of its weight. And so those who make these erroneous statements are deceived in the following way. First they assert that the force of the intelligence that causes the motion is so proportioned to the resistance of the heavens that it can move the heavens at the speed at which it now does, but at no greater speed: but if, by the addition of some star the resistance of the heavens were to be increased, then, they say, the motion of the heavens under the same motive force would have to become slower.

Now, in my opinion, they are led to believe this because they see about them how, if someone is turning a large wheel, and a great weight is then added to it on one side, he will have to work harder, or else the motion will become slower. But they do not observe that what causes such an effect is that the wheel is rotating about a center other than the center of the universe, so that, when the added weight has to be carried from the lowest to the highest point of the wheel, it then moves contrary to nature [i.e., by force], since it is moving upward and receding from the center of the universe.[4] But if the wheel were rotating about the center of the universe,[5] who would ever say that it was impeded by the weight, since the weight in its circular path would neither approach nor recede from the center. A similar argument holds for the heavens. For a star will be able to retard the motion only when it is being moved away from the place toward which it would naturally tend. But this never happens in a rotation that takes place about the center of the universe, for there never is upward and never downward motion. Therefore the motion will not be retarded by the addition of a star.

As for the second of the questions stated above,[6] this is not the

4. Strictly, Galileo's argument would not apply if the line joining the center of the universe and the center of the rotating wheel was perpendicular to the plane of the rotating wheel. But in such a case resistance at the point where the axis is supported would cause the motion to come to a halt, as indicated below.

5. Or, in general, if the axis of rotation passed through the center of the universe.

6. 305, above. The question is never taken up, but an analogous one is considered immediately below. Cf. also 309, below, and Benedetti, *Diversarum speculationum . . . liber*, pp. 285–86 (Koyré, *Études Galiléennes*, I, 45).

place to answer it. For we must first consider by what agency non-natural [i.e., forced] motion takes place.[7]

And in the case of the circular motion that does not take place about the center of the universe,[8] we must make a distinction with respect to the rotating body, viz., whether it consists of homogeneous or of heterogeneous parts.

Now if the body is of homogeneous parts, e.g., a marble sphere, rotating on an axis, such motion will be neither natural nor forced. For the center of gravity of the sphere neither approaches nor recedes from the center of the universe, and the weight of the parts of the sphere that are moving up is equal to the weight of the parts that are moving down, so that the sphere is always in equilibrium. And yet by accident such a rotation turns out to be a case of forced motion, because, of course, there is resistance at the supports of the axis. For since the sphere happens to be outside its proper place, it happens also to exert pressure and to require support. Hence the extremities of the axis of the sphere, by pressing down upon the points of support, impede the motion. But the finer and the smoother are the ends of the axis, the less resistance will they encounter: so that, if we imagine them to be indivisible,[9] no resistance will then arise from them. It also happens that such motion is retarded by the condition of the surface of the sphere, if it is rough and uneven. For the surrounding air and the air caught in the cavities of the surface will impede the motion, and not help it along, as someone has thought. This will be explained in its proper place.[10]

But suppose that the sphere is heterogeneous, and has its center of gravity outside its center of magnitude, and is rotated about its center of magnitude. In that case, quite apart from the accidental causes adduced above, there will be an essential reason why such a motion is not, as was the other, "neither natural nor forced," but instead is "sometimes natural and sometimes forced." For since the center of gravity in such a rotation describes a circle about the center of magnitude, it will be moving by force while it rises from its lowest to its highest position, since it is then receding from the center of the universe. And while it moves from the highest to the lowest position, its motion will surely be nat-

307

---

7. Ch. 17.
8. Or, more generally, circular motion in which the axis of rotation does not pass through the center of the universe.
9. I.e., as mathematical points.
10. See the beginning of the next chapter.

ural. But with the impetus it has received, it cannot be lifted forcibly to the same extent as it has fallen naturally. The reason for this will be explained in its proper place,[11] but because of this fact the difficulty in the ascent is greater than the downward tendency in the descent. Hence it follows, both for this [essential] reason and for the other accidental reasons, that the motion suggests the quality of the forced rather than of the natural.

11. This promise is not carried out.

Chapter [17]

By what agency projectiles are moved.

Aristotle, as in practically everything that he wrote about locomotion, wrote the opposite of the truth on this question too. And surely this is not strange. For who can arrive at true conclusions from false assumptions? Aristotle could not maintain his view that the mover must be in contact with the moving body, unless he said that projectiles are moved by the air. And he gave testimony of this opinion of his in many passages.[1]

308

And since we must refute this view, we shall first state it, but only in a summary way, for it is explained at considerable length by the commentators.

Aristotle holds that the mover, e.g., one who throws a stone, before he lets go of the stone, sets the contiguous parts of the air in motion; that these parts, similarly, move other parts, and these still others, and so on in succession; that the stone, after being released by the projector, is then moved along by those portions of air; and that thus the motion of the stone becomes, as it were, discontinuous, and is not a single motion but several.[2] Aristotle and his followers, who could not persuade themselves that a body could be moved by a force impressed upon it, or recognize what that force was, tried to take refuge in this view. But in order that the other view, the true one, may be made clear, we shall first seek to demolish completely this view of Aristotle. Then we shall, so far as we can, explain and illustrate with examples the other view, which concerns the impressed force.

And so, against Aristotle I argue as follows: Suppose the parts of air which move the body are *A, B, C, D,* and *E,* and suppose

1. Marginal note: "*Physics* 4.68 [215a14–17]; 8.82 [266b27–267a20]; *De Caelo* 3.28 [301b22–29]; *On Dreams* ch. 2 [459a29–b1]; *On Divination by Dreams* ch. 2, sec. 11, prob. 6 [464a6–9]" (F).
2. Marginal note: "*Physics* 8.28" (F). [28 seems to be a mistake for 82: cf. 267a12–14.]

A is in contact with the mover. Now either all of these parts are moved at the same time, or one part is moved after another. If *A, B, C, D,* and *E* are all moved at the same time, then I ask by what they are moved when the mover comes to rest; and in that case one must come to the notion of an impressed force. If, however, *A* is moved before *B*, then again I ask by what *B* is moved when *A* comes to rest. Furthermore, again according to Aristotle,[3] forced motion is swifter in the middle of the motion than at the beginning. Therefore part *C* of the air, under the impulse of *B*, is moved more swiftly than is *B*. Hence *C* will likewise move *D* more swiftly than *A, B, C, D,* and *E* have themselves been moved by *B*.[4] Hence *D* will also move *E* more swiftly than it [*D*] was moved by *C:* and so on in succession. Therefore forced motion will always be accelerated.[5]

Secondly, there is the argument of the arrow which is set in motion by the bowstring, even in the face of a strong north wind, and yet flies with great speed. My adversaries have no answer to this argument other than that, however hard the wind blows, air is nevertheless carried against the wind, having received the impetus from the bow. And they are not ashamed to utter such childishness. But what will they say to the following similar argument? Suppose a ship is propelled by oars against the current of a river, and the oars are then taken out of the water, and the ship moves for a considerable distance against the course of the water. Who is so blind as not to see that the water actually flows with very great force in the direction opposite [to that of the ship], and, furthermore, that this water, which is in contact with the ship, does not swerve at all from its natural course because of any impetus of the ship?[6]

309

Thirdly, if it is the medium that carries moving bodies along, how does it happen that when one shoots an iron ball, and, with the same shot of the cannon, [a ball of] wood, or tow, or some-

---

3. Marginal note: "De Caelo 2.35" (F). Actually Aristotle makes this statement (288a22) not of forced motion generally, but of the motion of missiles. Note that Galileo assumes the Aristotelian premise merely to refute Aristotle. He is not necessarily accepting the truth of the premise.

4. Parts of *B* are thought of as striking other parts of *B* and even as striking *A* in reverse.

5. And this would contradict Aristotle's assumption.

6. Marginal note: "When a piece of wood, falling naturally in air, falls into water, the medium has not, in that case, been moved by a projector; and the motive force which is 'natural' while the wood is in the air, passes into a force 'contrary to nature' when the wood is in water. The force remains in the same place, i.e., in the moving body itself, in which it was while the body was falling naturally in the air" (F).

thing light—the heavy object being the first out—how, I say, does it happen that the iron is flung a very great distance, while the tow, after following the iron for some distance, stops and falls to the ground? If, then, it is the medium that carries along both of them, why does it carry the lead or iron so far, but not the tow? Is it easier for the air to move the very heavy iron than the very light tow, or the wood?

Fourthly, Aristotle does not seem to be self-consistent. For he says (*De Caelo* 3.27):[7] "If what is moved is neither heavy nor light, its motion will be by force; and what is moved by force, and offers no resistance of heaviness or lightness, moves without end." And in the next passage he says that projectiles are carried along by the medium. But then, since air has neither weight nor lightness, once it is moved by the projector it will move endlessly and always at the same speed. And it will consequently also carry along projectiles in endless motion, and will never be weakened, since it always moves with the same force. But experience shows that the opposite of this happens.

In the fifth place, consider a marble sphere,[8] perfectly round and smooth, which can rotate on an axis the ends of which rest on two supports. Then suppose a mover comes who twists both ends of the axis with his finger tips. Surely in that case the sphere will rotate for a long time. Yet the air was not set in motion by the mover. Nor can the air act upon the sphere by driving it on, since the sphere never changes its position. And since it is perfectly smooth, it has no cavities into which the air can rush. In fact, the air around the sphere will remain quite motionless. This becomes clear if a flame is brought near the [rotating] sphere, for it will neither be extinguished nor disturbed.

These are the arguments by which we hold that that absurd view is adequately, and more than adequately, refuted—a view which those try to maintain who cannot satisfy themselves as to the nature of impressed force. But now, in order to explain our own view, let us first ask what is that motive force which is impressed by the projector upon the projectile. Our answer, then, is that it is a taking away of heaviness
310
when the body is hurled upward, and a taking away of lightness, when the body is hurled downward. But if a person is not surprised that fire can deprive iron of cold by introducing heat, he will not be surprised that the projector can, by hurling

7. 301b1–4.
8. A similar example is given by Buonamici, *De Motu* V. c. 36, p. 504 (as cited by Koyré, *Études Galiléennes*, I, 26).

a heavy body upward, deprive it of heaviness and render it light.

The body, then, is moved upward by the projector so long as it is in his hand and is deprived of its weight; in the same way the iron is moved, in an alterative motion,[9] towards heat, so long as the iron is in the fire and is deprived by it of its coldness. Motive force, that is to say lightness, is preserved in the stone,[10] when the mover is no longer in contact; heat is preserved in the iron after the iron is removed from the fire. The impressed force gradually diminishes in the projectile when it is no longer in contact with the projector; the heat diminishes in the iron, when the fire is not present.[11] The stone finally comes to rest; the iron similarly returns to its natural coldness. Motion is more strongly impressed by the same given force in a body that is more resistant than in one that is less resistant, e.g., in the stone, more than in light pumice; and, similarly, heat is more strongly impressed by the same fire upon very hard, cold iron, than upon weak and less cold wood.

It would be ridiculous to say that the air previously heated by the fire preserved the heat in the iron after the fire was extinguished or removed to a distance, for iron glows with heat even in the coldest air. And it is even more ridiculous to believe that motion is preserved in the projectile by air which is motionless or which even blows in the opposite direction. But who will not say that the iron is cooled more quickly in cold air by reason of the coldness of the air? And who of sound mind will not say that air impedes motion when it is either at rest or blows in the opposite direction?

But let me give another more beautiful example. Do you wonder what it is that passes from the hand of the projector and is impressed upon the projectile? Yet you do not wonder what passes from the hammer and is transferred to the bell of the clock, and how it happens that so loud a sound is carried over from the silent hammer to the silent bell, and is preserved in the bell when the hammer which struck it is no longer in contact. The bell is struck by the striking object; the stone is moved by the mover. The bell is deprived of its silence; the stone of its state of rest. A sonorous quality is imparted to the bell contrary to its natural silence; a motive quality is imparted to the stone con-

9. The Aristotelian concept of motion includes qualitative and quantitative change, as well as change of place.

10. E.g., if projected upward.

11. The same comparison is found in Buonamici, *De Motu* V. c. 36, p. 504 (quoted by Koyré, *Études Galiléennes*, I, 24). The analogies of both heat and sound are set down by Galileo in the memoranda (409–10).

trary to its state of rest. The sound is preserved in the bell, when the striking object is no longer in contact; motion is preserved in the stone when the mover is no longer in contact. The sonorous quality gradually diminishes in the bell; the motive quality gradually diminishes in the stone. But who of sound mind will say that it is the air that continues to strike the bell? For, in the first place, only one small portion of air is moved by the hammer. But if someone puts his hand on the bell, even on the side opposite the hammer, he will immediately feel a sharp, stinging, and numbing action that runs through all the metal. Secondly, if it is the air that strikes the bell and causes the sound in it, why is the bell silent even if the strongest wind is blowing? Can it be that the strong south wind, which churns up the whole sea and topples towers and walls, strikes [the bell] more gently than does the hammer, which hardly moves. In the third place, if it were the air that caused the sound in the bronze, rather than the bronze that caused the sound in the air, all bells of the same shape would emit the same sound; indeed, even a wooden bell, or at least a leaden or marble one, would produce as much sound as a bronze one.[12] But, finally, let those be still who keep saying that it is the air which causes the sound or carries the sound [to the bell]. For the bell vibrates as it emits the sound, and the vibration and sound remain in it and are preserved even when the striking agent is no longer in contact. But to ascribe to the air the setting in motion of such a great mass [i.e., the bell], when it [the air] has scarcely been moved itself by the hammer, exceeds all reason. To return, then, to our point, why are they puzzled that a motive quality can be impressed in a body by a mover, but not that a sound and a certain motion of vibration can be impressed in a bell by a hammer?

But, what is more, they say that they cannot conceive that a heavy stone should be able to become light by receiving a motive force from a projector. But this force, since it is lightness, will indeed render the body in motion light by inhering in it. Yet these same people say that it is utterly ridiculous to suppose that a stone has become light after its upward motion and weighs less than before. But their judgment of things is not based on a sober and reasonable consideration. For I too would not say that a stone, after its [upward] motion, has become [permanently] light. I would say rather that it retains[13] its natural weight, just

---

12. The same point is made in the memoranda (410.8).
13. I.e., potentially.

311 (margin)

as the hot glowing iron is devoid of coldness but, after the heat [is used up], it resumes the same coldness that is its own. And there is no reason for us to be surprised that the stone, so long as it is moving [upward], is light. Indeed, between a stone in that act of motion [upward] and any other light body it will not be possible to assign any difference. For since we call light that which moves upward, and the [projected] stone does move upward, the stone is therefore light so long as it moves upward.

But you will say that that is light which moves upward *naturally,* not that which does so by force. But I say that that is naturally light which moves upward naturally. And I say that that is light preternaturally, or accidentally, or by *312* force, whose upward motion is contrary to nature, accidental, and by force: and such is the stone which is set in motion by force. And in the case of this stone its natural and intrinsic weight is lost in the same way as when it is placed in media heavier than itself. For a stone which floats, let us say, in mercury and does not sink, loses all its weight; indeed, it loses weight and assumes lightness to such an extent that it promptly resists even a great deal of weight that comes to it externally—e.g., if one tries to press it down. Wood, too, becomes so light in water that it cannot be kept down except by force. And yet, neither the stone nor the wood loses its natural weight, but, on being taken from those heavier media, they both resume their proper weight. In the same way, a projectile, when freed from the projecting force, manifests, by descending, its true and intrinsic weight.

Furthermore, those who oppose our views, ask skeptically in what part of the [projected] body the force I speak of is received, on the surface, in the center, or in some other part. My brief answer to them is this. Let them first tell me in what part of the iron the heat is received, and I shall then tell them where the motive force is received. And I shall place it where they place the heat. If the heat is received only on the surface, then I shall say that the force is received only on the surface; and if in the center, then in the center. And if they say that the heat is received where previously there was cold, I shall say that extrinsic lightness entered those parts in which intrinsic heaviness previously resided.

Finally, my opponents express wonder that the same hand has the ability of impressing now lightness, now heaviness, and now even that which seems to be neither heavy nor light.[14] But why

14. The same hand that can throw an object up or down can project it horizontally or even let it fall or rise by itself.

don't they express wonder instead that they now want a certain thing, and a little later they don't want that same thing; that they sometimes believe something, sometimes have hesitation and doubt about it, and sometimes even disbelieve it? But if, as in these cases, it depends on the will that we can now lift our arm, then lower it, then move it in various directions, and if the arm, thus governed by our will, has the power now to press down, and now to lift, why need we wonder that that which is pressed down by the arm receives weight while that which is lifted is cloaked with lightness?

But, since it is not foreign to my subject, let me not pass over in silence a certain quite common error. Some people *313* believe that, since air and water are fluids, they can be very easily and swiftly moved, particularly air. And because of this, these people have held that the projector moves the air more than he does the projectile, and that the air carries along the projectile. But the facts are quite different, as those people themselves sometimes admit. For, with their leader Aristotle, they sometimes say that the air, in order to be able to carry along the projectiles, moves very swiftly by reason of its lightness, since it offers practically no resistance. But at other times they say that that which has neither heaviness nor lightness cannot be moved, because that which is moved must offer resistance. In these statements they affirm and deny the same propositions according to what suits their purpose better. But the fact is that the lighter the body is, the more is it moved while it is in contact with the mover, but, on being released by the mover, it retains for only a short time the impetus it has received. This is clear if someone throws a feather, using as much force as if one had to throw a pound of lead. For he will more easily move the feather than the lead, but the impressed force will be retained in the lead for a longer time than in the feather, and he will throw the lead much farther. But if it were the air that carried the projectile along, who would ever believe that the air could carry the lead more easily than the feather? We see therefore that the lighter a thing is, the more easily is it moved; but the less does it retain the impetus it has received. And so, since the air, as was shown above, has no weight in its own proper place, it will be moved very easily, but will not at all retain the impetus it has received. And we shall show below why light bodies do not retain this impetus.

Nor is there any force in the example they give of the pebble thrown into the lake—the pebble by which, they tell us, the water is moved in a [widening] circle over great distances.[15] For, in the first place, it is false to say that the water is moved. This is clear if there are pieces of wood or straw floating on the water; for they will not at all be moved from their position by the eddies of water, but will be lifted only a little by the wavelets and will not follow the circumference of the [widening] circles. Secondly, the analogy does not hold good in the case of air, for the surface of the air is not moved by the projector, while it is only the surface of the water that is moved by the pebble. And this topmost surface of the water is raised and lowered only for the reason that it offers resistance to keep it from being raised and carried into the place of air. But the motive force cannot be impressed in the middle of the air, because in that case the air offers no resistance, since it is not being thrust from its place into the place of another medium. This would also be the case in the middle of the water, which would not retain the impetus it had received, since its motion would have no tendency. It would not have the tendency of natural motion, because it would not be moving toward its own place, since it was already there; nor would it have the tendency of forced motion, since it would not be thrust into the place of another medium.

314

This was the common error of those who said that projectiles were moved by the medium. And it sometimes happens that certain opinions, however false they may be, attain long-standing currency among men, because at first sight they offer some appearance of truth, and no one bothers to examine whether they are worthy of belief. An instance of this sort of thing is the belief about things that are under the water. Common opinion asserts that these objects appear larger than they really are.[16] But when I could not discover a reason for such an effect, I finally had recourse to experiment and found that a denarius coin at rest in deep water did not at all appear larger [than actual size], but rather appeared smaller. And so, I believe that the one who first put forth this [mistaken] opinion, was led to it in the summertime when plums or other fruits are sometimes placed in a glass vessel full of water, the shape of which vessel resembles the surface of a conoid. These pieces of fruit would appear far larger

---

15. Cf. the memorandum (411.6): "We must refute as false the view of those who say that when a pebble is thrown in water, the water thereafter moves by itself in a [widening] circle."

16. Marginal addition: "And there is another common error, the error of certain ones who say that any part of a mirror reflects the whole image" (F).

than they really are to those who view them in such a way that the visual rays pass through the [curved] glass. But the shape of the vessel, not the water, is the cause of this effect, as we have explained in our commentaries on the *Almagest* of Ptolemy, which, with God's help, will be published in a short time.[17] And an indication of this is the fact that if the eye is placed above the water in such a way that the plum can be seen without the interference of the glass medium, it does not appear larger.

Let us, therefore, conclude finally that projectiles can in no way be moved by the medium, but only by a motive force impressed by the projector. And let us now go on to show that this force is gradually diminished, and that in a case of forced motion no two points can be assigned in which the motive force is the same.

17. These commentaries were never published and have never been found.

Chapter [18]

In which it is shown that the motive force is gradually weakened in the moving body.

Since it was settled in the previous chapter that projectiles are moved by an impressed force, it is clear that forced motion is one and continuous, and not many and discontinuous, as Aristotle believed.[1] And since this is so, and since forced motion is not endless, it must follow that that force, impressed by the projector, is continuously diminished in the projectile, and that there cannot exist two points of time in the course of that motion such that the motive force is the same in both and not weaker [at the later point]. That this may be seen even more clearly, I shall use the following demonstration, assuming, first, that the same body, in the same medium and over the same line, is moved by the same force with the same velocity.

With this assumption, let there be a line *ab* over which motion takes place, and suppose the motion takes place from *a* to *b*;[2] and, if it is possible, let there be found on line *ab* two points, *c* and *d*, at which there is the same motive force. Since, then, the motive force is the same at *c* as at *d*, the medium the same, the body the same, and the line in which the motion takes place also the same, it follows that the body will move from point *d* at the same speed as it moved from point *c*. But it moved from point *c* in such a way that it was carried from *c* to *d* always at the same

315

1. *Physics* 267b15.

2. From the context and the diagram it is clear that Galileo is speaking specifically of forced upward motion.

speed and the force did not become weaker. Therefore it will also be moved from d on a line equal to line cd with the same speed, since the same impressed force remains. For there is no reason why the force should remain the same from c to d, but not from d on a line toward b equal to line cd, since the force, the body, the medium, and the line of motion are all the same. Therefore, by repeating the same argument, it will be shown that the forced motion is never diminished, but continues always and without end at the same speed, with the motive force always remaining the same. But this surely is most absurd. It is therefore not true that in a forced motion two points can be assigned in which the impelling force remains the same. Which was to be proved.

Chapter [19]

In which the cause of the acceleration of natural motion towards the end is set forth, a cause far different from that which the Aristotelians assign.

The reason why the speed of natural motion is increased toward the end is certainly more difficult to discover than to explain. Either no one has thus far discovered it or, if at times someone has hinted at it, he has presented it in imperfect and defective form, and it has not been accepted by philosophers in general. Now, while engaged in seeking for the cause of this effect [of acceleration], which I shall not call surprising but necessary—for the cause assigned by Aristotle[1] never appealed to me—I was troubled for a long time, and did not find anything that fully satisfied me. And, indeed, when I discovered an explanation that was completely sound (at least in my own judgment), at first I rejoiced. But when I examined it more carefully, I mistrusted its apparent freedom from any difficulty. And now, finally, having ironed out every difficulty with the passage of time, I shall publish it in its exact and fully proved form. But according to my custom I shall first consider what force there is in the explanation which is given by Aristotle.

In the first place, it should be known that certain recent writers assert that Aristotle attributed the cause of acceleration to the parts of the air which rush to fill the void behind the moving body and strike the back of the body. By reason of this striking,

316

1. Marginal note: "Aristotle held that the speed of motion is increased because the weight of the body is more concentrated and strengthened as the body approaches its proper place. See Saint Thomas, *Comm. on De Caelo* 1.88 *fin.*" (F). [See *De Caelo* 277a29–33.]

they themselves say, natural motion is accelerated. But that Aristotle did not hold such a view can be clearly ascertained from what we read in *De Caelo* 1.89[2] where in clear language he says: "Natural motion is not accelerated by extrusion, as some have believed; for in that case it would be forced motion, which is diminished toward the end, not augmented as is natural motion." It is clear, then, that Aristotle not only does not hold this view, but even rejects it. And it deserves to be rejected. For, with regard to what they say about a void, either such a void is left in the rear of the moving body, or it is not. If not, why do they say that the air rushes down to fill the void? But if a void is left, why do they not also say that the body moves back to fill the void, and that consequently the motion is rather retarded by this cause and not accelerated?

Secondly, consider a body concerning which there could be no question [about the impossibility] of its being struck from behind by the air—a body such as a solid rhombus consisting of two cones and tapering out on both sides into a very sharp point. This body surely will not be able to be struck [from behind] by air since its shape does not have anything against which the air could strike.

Thirdly, objects which are moved by force, do not move more swiftly than that by which they are moved. But the air, in moving toward the back of the moving body, is moved by force: for in its own region it is naturally at rest. Therefore it cannot move more swiftly than that by which it is moved. But it is moved by the falling body. Therefore the air will not move more swiftly than the falling body. But if it does not move more swiftly, it certainly will not be able to strike it. For if someone wants to strike a person running in the same direction as he is himself, it is necessary for him to run faster than that person and to speed up in the same direction as that person. But this does not happen in the case of a body moving naturally. On the contrary, the air moves in the opposite direction. Thus, if a sphere *abc* falls, the surrounding air from parts *b* and *c*, rushing in to the back of body *a*, will move upward with respect to the downward motion of the sphere. This is also admitted by those writers when they declare that the medium resists motion because it must be divided: for if the medium must be divided, it certainly will not move in the same direction as the moving body. Therefore it will either be at rest, or it will move in the opposite

317

---

2. Cf. 277b1–8.

direction to the moving body. At all events, even if we insist that it moves in the same direction as the moving body, it will move more slowly. And since this is so, how will it accelerate the motion?

Fourthly, those writers are not looking for an essential reason for the acceleration of motion, but only an accidental reason. For it is by accident that a body moves in a plenum, and that its speed is hindered or helped along by a medium. But what we ask is why a body in natural motion, as it moves naturally by reason of its own weight, quite apart from any consideration of medium, moves more quickly at the end than in the middle of the motion, and more quickly in the middle than in the beginning; and how a consideration of motion shows that, at the beginning, the motion must be slower.

So much in answer to those who espouse this view.

Others have said that the body moves more swiftly at the end of the motion for the reason that the body must then cleave fewer parts of the medium; and they have felt that it moves along more swiftly since it encounters less resistance. Now this view is not only false, but ridiculous. For if it were true, it would follow that a stone falling from the top of a very high tower would, as it moved past the middle of the tower, have a lesser speed than would the same body if it fell from a very low place to the ground. And for this reason it would [in the former case] produce a lesser impact.

That this may be more clearly understood, let there be a line *abc,* and let *ac* be far greater than *cb.* I say, then, that [on the theory under discussion] if a stone fell from *a* it would move more slowly when it was around *c,* than the same stone, if let fall from *c,* would move in the vicinity of *b.* The reason would, of course, be that the body would have to divide fewer parts of the air when it was near *b,* after having been let fall from *c,* than when it was near *c,* after coming from *a.* It can also be added that [on the theory under discussion] a stone falling from *a* would strike the ground with the same force as it would if coming from *c.* And the reason would be that the stone falling from *a* would, when it was a little below *c,* not be moving faster than the stone falling from *c* when *it* was a little below *c:* for in the former case no fewer parts of the air would remain to be divided than in the latter case. And these writers themselves say that the *318* speed of the motion depends on this cleaving [of the medium]. Now there is no one who is unaware how incongruous all these arguments are.

But, leaving aside the opinions of others, we shall use the following analytic method to track down what we believe to be the true cause of this effect [i.e., of acceleration of natural motion]. And let us speak of natural downward motion that proceeds from weight: for, when we have solved this case, we shall determine the case of upward motion by a reversal of the argument.[3] Since, then, a heavy falling body moves more slowly at the beginning, it follows that the body is less heavy at the beginning of its motion than in the middle or at the end. For we know definitely, from what was proved at the beginning of this book,[4] that speed and slowness are a consequence of weight and lightness. If, then, we can find how and why it is that the body is less heavy at the beginning of the motion, we shall definitely have found the reason why it falls more slowly. But the natural and intrinsic weight of the body has surely not been diminished, since neither its volume nor its density has been diminished. We are left with the conclusion that that diminution of weight is contrary to nature and accidental. If, then, we have found that the weight of the body is diminished unnaturally and from without, we will then surely have found what we seek. But that weight is not diminished by the weight of the medium, for the medium is the same in the beginning of the motion as in the middle. The conclusion remains that the weight of the body is diminished by some external force coming to it from without—for only in these two ways does it happen that the body becomes accidentally light.[5]

If, then, we find out how a body can be lightened by an external force, we will have, in that case, discovered the cause of the slowness. Now the force impressed by a projector not only at

3. Or, possibly, "by a contrary argument," to *deny* such acceleration. Actually, Galileo does not take up the case of so-called "natural" upward motion from the point of view of acceleration. But in the reworking of some of the material of ch. 12, though he lays the groundwork for an explanation of acceleration in this case, he finally seems to deny its existence altogether (365.27 ff., translated in Appendix I, *fin.*, below).

4. E.g., ch. 7.

5. Marginal addition: "The weight of the body can be accidentally diminished in two ways—either by the weight of the medium or by an impressed force—though Benedict Pererio [Pereira] declared that the medium could not diminish weight, when he wrote in opposition to Aristotle as follows: 'Aristotle does not properly conclude that, because velocity increases in natural motion, the weight in the body must also increase. For if a stone moves over a path the first part of which is denser and thicker, and the latter part rarer and thinner, the motion will doubtless be speedier at the end, and this will not happen because of an increase in weight.' Book 14, ch. 3 *fin.*" (F). Cf. the longer quotation in the memoranda (411.18), where Galileo calls Pereira's reasoning erroneous. The work, *De communibus omnium rerum naturalium principiis et affectionibus libri XV,* had been published at Paris in 1579 and 1585. There is also a 1595 edition.

times diminishes the weight of a heavy body, but often even renders it so light that it flies up with great speed. Let us see, therefore, and carefully investigate whether possibly that very force is the cause of the diminishing of the weight of the body at the beginning of its motion. And in fact it definitely is that force impressed by a projector that makes natural motion slower at the beginning.

319 　　Let us hasten to explain how it is able to accomplish this. For a heavy body to be able to be moved upward by force, an impelling force greater than the resisting weight is required; otherwise the resisting weight could not be overcome, and, consequently, the body could not move upward. That is, the body moves upward, provided the impressed motive force is greater than the resisting weight. But since that force, as has been shown, is continuously weakened, it will finally become so diminished that it will no longer overcome the weight of the body and will not impel the body beyond that point. And yet, this does not mean that at the end of the forced motion this impressed force will have been completely destroyed, but merely that it will have been so diminished that it no longer exceeds the weight of the body but is just equal to it. To put it in a word, the force that impels the body upward, which is lightness, will no longer be dominant in the body, but it will have been reduced to parity with the weight of the body. And at that time, in the final moment of the forced motion, the body will be neither heavy nor light.

But beyond that, as the impressed force characteristically continues to decrease, the weight of the body begins to be predominant, and consequently the body begins to fall. Yet there still remains, at the beginning of this descent, a considerable force that impels the body upwards, which constitutes lightness, though this force is no longer greater than the heaviness of the body. For this reason the essential weight of the body is diminished by this lightness and consequently the motion is slower at the beginning. Furthermore, since that external force continues to be weakened, the weight of the body, being offset by diminishing resistance, is increased, and the body moves faster and faster.

This is what I consider to be the true cause of the acceleration of motion. After I had thought it out, and happened to be reading, two months later, what Alexander says on the subject, I learned from him that this had also been the view of the very able philosopher Hipparchus, who is cited by the learned Ptolemy. Hipparchus is, in fact, greatly esteemed and is extolled with the highest praises by Ptolemy throughout the whole text of his *Almagest*. Now according to Alexander,[6] Hipparchus too believed that this was the cause of the acceleration of natural motion, but, since he added nothing beyond what we said above, the view seemed imperfect and was thought to deserve rejection by philosophers. For it seemed to apply only to those cases of natural motion [e.g., downward] which were preceded by forced motion [upward], and not to be applicable to that [natural] motion which does not follow [an opposite] forced motion.[7]

320   Indeed, the philosophers were not content to reject the view as imperfect; they considered it actually false, and not even true in the case where the [natural] motion was preceded by forced motion. But we shall also add the material which was not explained by Hipparchus, and shall show that the same cause holds good also in the case of [natural] motion not preceded by forced motion. And we shall try to free our explanation from every fallacy. I would not, however, say that Hipparchus was wholly undeserving of criticism: for he left undetected a difficulty of great importance. But I shall merely add the material which is lacking and reveal the splendor of the truth.

I say, then, that those [natural] motions which have not been preceded by a forced motion are also slower at the beginning for the same reason [as the other natural motions]. For even in the

6. In Simplicius, *Comm. on Aristotle De Caelo* 264.25 ff. (Heiberg): "Hipparchus in his work entitled *On bodies carried down by their weight* declares that, in the case of earth thrown upward, the projecting force is the cause of the upward motion, so long as the projecting force overpowers the downward tendency of the projectile; and that, to the extent that this projecting force predominates, the object moves more swiftly upwards. Then, as this force is diminished, (1) the upward motion proceeds, but no longer at the same rate, (2) the body then moves downward under the influence of its own internal impulse, even though the original projecting force lingers in some measure, and (3) as this force continues to diminish, the object moves downward always more swiftly, and most swiftly when this force is entirely lost.

"Now Hipparchus asserts that the same cause operates in the case of bodies let fall from above. For, he says, the force which held them back remains with them up to a certain point, and this is the restraining factor which accounts for the slower movement at the start of the fall."

7. Alexander (in Simplicius, *Comm. on Aristotle de Caelo* 265.11 ff.) takes issue with the view expressed in the second paragraph of the preceding note. As can be seen from that paragraph, it is questionable that Galileo knew the material at first hand, for he seems to assume that Alexander criticized Hipparchus for not treating the case of free fall from rest.

Cf. also Galileo's memorandum (411.1): "Alexander thought that he had successfully refuted the opinion of Hipparchus on acceleration at the end of natural motion, when he adduced in opposition the case of natural motion not preceded by forced motion. And, indeed, even Hipparchus did not observe that forced motion preceded every case of natural motion, as we have made clear."

Cf. the discussion in the *Discourses*, E.N., VIII, 201 ff.

case of those motions preceded by a forced motion, the body begins to move from an [instantaneous][8] state of rest, not from a forced motion. Thus, when a stone, which had been thrown up, begins to move down from that extreme point at which equilibrium occurs between impelling force and resisting weight (i.e., from rest), it begins to fall. This fall is the same as if the stone dropped from someone's hand. For even when no force impelling the stone upward has been impressed on it, and it falls from the hand, it leaves with an [upward] force impressed on it equal to its own weight. For when the stone is at rest in someone's hand, we must not say that in that case the holder of the stone is impressing no force upon it. Indeed, since the stone presses downward with its own weight, it must be impelled upward by the hand with a force exactly equal, neither larger nor smaller. For if the force with which the hand impels the stone upward were greater than the weight of the stone, the resisting stone would be lifted by[9] the hand, and it would not be at rest, as we assume. And, on the other hand, if the downward pressure of the stone were greater than the lifting force of the hand, the stone would tend to move downward. But we are assuming that the stone is at rest in the hand. Therefore a force that impels upward is impressed on the stone by the hand or by whatever else controls the hand, and this force is exactly equal to the weight of the stone that tends downward.

Nevertheless the stone is not lifted up because, as we have said, the force that impels [the stone upwards] cannot overcome the resisting weight, since it is not greater than that weight. It is clear, then, that when the stone drops from the hand, it has, as it leaves, an [upward] force impressed on it equal to its own weight, no differently from what happens when the stone, having finished an upward motion, begins to move downward. For in that case, too, when it leaves its [instantaneous] state of rest,[10] it leaves having an [upward] force [impressed on it] equal to its weight. Hence, it is for the same cause that, just as in the latter type of [natural] motion [i.e., preceded by forced motion], so in the former [i.e., not preceded by forced motion], the body moves more slowly at the beginning.

321   But, in order to make still clearer my explanation of the whole matter, I shall discuss a particular example. Let there be a line *ab* upon which forced motion takes place from

8. Cf. ch. 20, below.
9. Or "from."
10. I.e., at the highest point of a vertically upward motion.

a to *b,* and natural motion from *b* to *a.* Let *c* be the moving body
with weight 4. Hence, for body *c* to move upward, a motive force
greater than its weight must be impressed upon it. And it would
not be moved by an equal force: for it would then be neither
heavy nor light, since its weight would be just equal to the impressed force, which is lightness. Suppose, then, that the force
which can project *c* as far as *b* is 8. Now since the motive force is
continuously diminishing, as we have shown above, and is unable
to move *c* unless it is greater than the weight of that body, it is
clear that, when *c* arrives at *b,* the impressed force will be equal
to the weight of *c.* For it will not be less, since then it would not
have driven *c* as far as *b;* nor will it be greater, because then it
would be driving *c* still farther. It must therefore be equal. And
so, when *c* is at *b* it has an [upward] force impressed on it equal
to its own weight, namely, 4.

But since this force continues to be gradually weakened and is
in the process of steady diminution, *c* changes over to downward
motion. Therefore, when *c* begins to fall from the first point *b,*
it leaves *b* with an [opposing] impressed force equal to its own
weight; and consequently it will move very slowly at the beginning of such a motion. But the more the opposing force is decreased, and, consequently, the weight increased, the swifter is
the motion that takes place. Again, if an impressed force of 8
projects *c* as far as *b,* it is clear that a force can be impressed upon
c such that it would project *c* only as far as *d.* And this force will
certainly be smaller than 8, yet greater than 4, for the resistant
weight of *c* is 4. Furthermore, a force can be impressed upon *c*
great enough to project *c* only as far as *e.* And this force, in its
turn, will be smaller than that which projects *c* as far as *d,* but
still greater than 4. For *c* cannot be moved [upward] by a force
equal to 4. Similarly, a force will be able to be impressed on
c sufficient to project *c* upward from *a* over every distance on *ae,*
no matter how small. But such a force, since it moves *c* upward,
will always be greater than 4. And every force which is less than
4 not only fails to project *c* upward, but cannot stop it from falling, since this force is overcome by the greater weight. It follows,
necessarily, that an impressed force of 4 will just sustain *c.*

322

Hence, when *c* is at rest, there will be on it an impressed force of 4 tending to drive it upward. And if it is released
by the agency that is impressing this force on it, it will begin to
fall back possessing an impressed force of 4. Therefore, it will not
again move upward after this retreat, but will fall very slowly at

the beginning and then move downward more swiftly according as the force opposing that motion becomes weaker.

We have no hesitation in asserting that this is the true, essential, and foremost cause that explains why natural motion is slower at the beginning. Those who examine it properly and fairly will, no doubt, accept it and embrace it as completely true. But could these results be attained by an easier method? They could, indeed, and could easily become familiar to one who considers the subject physically. For, pray, do not the following two propositions merge into one: "Forced motion is slow at the end. Therefore, natural motion is slow at the beginning"? For natural motion follows upon forced motion, and the end of the forced is linked with the beginning of the natural. But the cause of the slowness of forced motion at the end is the smallness of the amount by which the projecting force exceeds the resistant weight, i.e., by which the cause of forced motion exceeds the cause of natural motion. Therefore, similarly, we must hold that the cause of the slowness of natural motion at its beginning is the smallness of the amount by which the cause of natural motion exceeds the cause of forced motion, i.e., by which the weight that presses the body down exceeds the lightness, that is to say, the impressed force, which impels the body up.

You can therefore see how well propositions that are true fit in with one another. And from this review anyone will easily be able to understand that these are really not two contrary motions, but rather a certain motion composed of a forced and a natural motion. For these local motions somehow depend on certain other alterative motions,[11] so long as intrinsic heaviness and extraneous lightness (for we shall hereafter call the impressed force lightness) are mingled in the moving body. And from this mingling it follows, and in a sense accidentally, that the body moves now up and now down. For when there is more lightness than heaviness in the mixture, an effect of lightness will result from it, namely, upward motion. But if, with the reduction of lightness, there is more heaviness in the body, an effect of heaviness, i.e., downward motion, will result. But that alterative motion, when the body changes from lightness to heaviness, is a single and continuous motion. Just as when water accidentally becomes cold from hot, it moves in a single motion toward coldness, and its motion from hot to warm is not different from its motion from warm to cold; so, too, when a body changes from light to neither

11. See 310, above.

heavy nor light, the motion is not separate from the motion in
which it changes from neither heavy nor light to heavy.
323   So far, then, are these motions from being contraries, that they are actually only one, continuous, and
coterminous. Hence also the effects which flow from these causes
cannot be rightly called contraries, since contrary effects depend
on contrary causes. Hence the upward motion cannot rightly be
called contrary to the ensuing downward motion—both of which
motions proceed from motion [i.e., change] in the mixture of
lightness and heaviness. And from this it can easily be deduced
that [an interval of] [12] rest does not intervene at the turning point
[i.e., from upward to downward motion]. For if there were [an
interval of] rest at that point, it would also be necessary for [an
interval of] rest to occur in that motion [i.e., change] in the mixture of heaviness and lightness, when the lightness came into
equality with the heaviness. For the body can only then be at rest
when the projecting force neither overcomes nor is overcome by
[the weight of the body]. But, as we have already explained, that
motion of change from light to heavy is one and continuous, just
as is the change from hot to cold, since it does not come to rest
for any [interval of] time. Hence also the local motions which
emanate from that motion [of change from light to heavy] will
be one and continuous. But this view, since it goes counter to the
general opinion—it is generally believed that there is [an interval
of] rest at the turning point—will be considered in the next chapter, where we shall first examine and refute the opposite view and
make our own position still stronger.

12. As opposed to instantaneous rest. See the next chapter, especially its conclusion. Cf. 320, above.

Chapter [20]

In which, in opposition to Aristotle and the general view, it is shown that at the turning point [an interval of] rest does not occur.

Aristotle and his followers believed that two contrary motions—
he defines contrary motions as those which tend toward opposite
goals—could in no way be continuous with each other. And
therefore they believed that, when a stone is projected upward and
then falls back over the same path, it must necessarily remain at
rest at the turning point. The chief argument with which Aris-

totle tries[1] to prove this is as follows. "Whatever[2]
324   moves by approaching some point and then moving
away from that same point, using it as an end and as
a beginning, will not move away from it, unless it has first
stopped at it. But that which moves to the farthest point of a line
and then moves back from that point, uses that point both as an end
and as a beginning. It must therefore remain stationary between

1. Marginal note: *"Physics* 8.65" [262a, b] (F).
2. The remainder of this paragraph and all of the next two paragraphs are on
a separate sheet and are substituted for the following passage, which is deleted
in the manuscript:
" 'A body in motion uses the extreme point of its motion as beginning, middle,
and end. And therefore the body makes two things out of what is one, as if a
person were, in thought, to consider one as two. It follows, therefore, that the
body must remain at rest at that extreme point, since the same thing is both the
end of one motion and the beginning of the contrary motion; and between the
instant at which the one ends and the instant at which the other begins, an
intermediate time is required.'
"This is the one consideration that might cause some difficulty. And to overcome this difficulty, my argument is as follows: In the first place, Aristotle said:
'The body uses one extremity as beginning, middle, and end; therefore it remains at rest at that point.' I deny the premise, for it is false to say that the
body uses [the extremity] as middle, beginning, and end; and Aristotle has not
proved it. Hence he seems to be guilty of circular reasoning. For I do not see of
what thing it is that [the body] uses [the extremity] as a middle—unless he
means it uses it as the middle of a state of rest, so that his argument takes the
following form: 'The body uses the farthest extremity as beginning, middle, and
end of its state of rest at the extremity. Therefore it is at rest at the extremity.'
In this form the argument would surely be a begging of the question or a case
of circular reasoning. For the question at issue is: does the state of rest of the
body at the extreme point have a beginning, middle, and end, i.e., is there
really [an interval of] rest? It is true, then, that the body uses the extremity as
an end and as a beginning, but not as a middle. But you will say: 'Between a
beginning and an end there must be a middle.' I answer that this is true between
a beginning and an end which are the beginning and the end of the same thing.
Such a thing, if it has a beginning and an end, must have a middle. But it is not
necessary that there be a middle between the beginning of one thing and the
end of another. Hence it is not necessary that there be [an interval of] time
between the end of forced motion and the beginning of natural motion, which
are extremities of two *different* things. As an example of this, suppose that lines
ab and *bc* meet at point *b*. Point *b* is an extremity of both these lines. And if *a*
is the beginning of a line, *b* will be the end; and if *c* is the end of the other line,
b will also be its beginning. Therefore *b* is an end and a beginning with respect
to different things. Yet who would say that between this beginning and this end
there would have to be a middle? And our view is the same with respect to the
final instant of one motion and the initial instant of a second motion. Just as in
the case of the lines *abc, b* is taken as two points and yet no line intervenes
between these two points, so also we consider the last instant of one motion as
two instants, and yet there is no [interval of] time between these instants. And
just as the two lines *ab* and *cb* terminate in a single point *b,* and there are really
two termini but not two [separate] points, so the last instant is really the
terminus of the times of both contrary motions; yet it does not follow that they
are two [separate] instants. We concede, then, that time intervenes between two
[separate] instants, just as a line does between two [separate] points. But we

the motion toward and the motion away from the point."[3] Aristotle proves his major premise thus: "Whoever treats something both as beginning and as end, makes what is one in number two in logic, just as the person who in thought takes a point, which is one and the same numerically, and makes it two in logic, namely the end of one thing and the beginning of a second thing. But if something uses one thing as two it must necessarily remain stationary there; for there is [an interval of] time between the two."

325

Such is Aristotle's argument. But how weak it is will soon be clear. For, as he himself holds, the moving body makes use of a point on the line of its motion,[4] i.e., one point, numerically, for what are two things in logic, for a beginning and an end. Yet there is no line between these two things, since they are only one in number. And why, similarly, will the same body not use the same instant (one, in number) as two in logic, namely, for the end of the time of moving toward [the turning point] and for the beginning of the time of moving away [from it], so that between these instants that are two in logic, no time intervenes, since they are only one in number?

There is no compelling reason why this should not be the case, especially since Aristotle himself holds that what is true of a line is true also of time and motion. If, then, on the same line the same point, numerically, is both the end of one motion and the beginning of a second, and if, nevertheless, it is not necessary that a line form a connection between this beginning and that end, then, in the same way, the same instant numerically, will, in logic, be the end of one time and the beginning of a second time, and it will not be necessary for time to intervene between the two. It is clear, then, that the refutation of Aristotle's argument can be neatly derived from the propositions of that same argument. Hence, since the argument no longer has compelling force for us, let us see whether we can construct arguments for the opposite view that are more sharply convincing.

So much in opposition to Aristotle. But in order for us to show by other arguments that [an interval of] rest does not occur at

---

deny that an instant, even if it is taken as the terminus of two or even of a thousand intervals of time, is itself [an interval of] time. In the same way, even if the same point is taken as a thousand termini of a thousand lines, there will be no line between these points" (F).

3. Cf. 262b2–8, 23–26.

4. The case of reflected motion is assumed, e.g., forced vertical upward, followed by natural vertical downward, motion.

the turning point, and that there need not be such rest between contrary motions, consider these additional arguments.

Secondly, suppose that some continuum, such as the whole of line *ab*, moves in the direction of *b* in a motion like a forced motion which becomes continuously slower. And while the line so moves, suppose that a body, say *c*, moves on the same line in the opposite direction, from *b* to *a*. But let this motion be like a natural motion, that is, one that is accelerated. And let the motion of the line at the beginning be faster than the motion of *c* at the beginning. Now it is clear that at the beginning *c* will move in the same direction as that in which the line moves, because the motion by which it is carried in the opposite direction is slower than the motion of the line. And yet, since the motion of the line becomes slower and the [leftward component of the] motion of *c* becomes faster, at some moment *c* will actually move toward the left, and will thus make the change from rightward to leftward motion over the same line. And yet it will not be at rest for any [interval of] time at the point where the change occurs. And

326

the reason for this is that it cannot be at rest unless the line moves to the right at the same speed as body *c* moves to the left. But it will never happen that this equality will continue over any interval of time, since the speed of one motion is continuously diminished, and that of the other continuously increased. Hence it follows that *c* will change from one motion to its contrary with no intervening state of rest.

My third argument can be drawn from a certain rectilinear motion which Nicholas Copernicus in his *De Revolutionibus* compounds from two circular motions. There are two circles [the center of] each of which is carried on the circumference of the other. When one circle moves more swiftly than the other, a point on the circumference of the first circle moves in a straight line continuously back and forth over the same path.[5] And yet it cannot be said that the point is at rest at the extremities, since it is carried continuously by the circumference of the circle.

My fourth argument is the well-known one about a large stone falling from a tower. A little pebble is forcibly thrown up from below against it, but the stone will not be sufficiently blocked by the pebble so as to allow the pebble to be at rest for

---

5. *De Revolutionibus*, Book III, ch. 4. There is an analogous and simpler example in Benedetti, *Diversarum speculationum . . . liber*, p. 183 (cited by Koyré, *Études Galiléennes*, I, 51), in which one end of a rigid bar is attached to a point (other than the center) of a continuously rotating circle, and the other end moves back and forth along the same straight line.

any interval of time. Hence the pebble will surely not remain at rest at the farthest point of its upward motion, and, despite what Aristotle said, it will use that farthest point as two termini, namely, of upward motion and of downward motion. And the last instant is taken twice, viz., as the end of one interval of time and as the beginning of the other.

But in order to escape from this argument my adversaries declare that the large stone is at rest, and so they believe that they have answered the argument. But, so that they may not believe this in the future (unless they are thoroughly obstinate), I shall add the following to my argument. Suppose that those stones which move with contrary motions move not up and down but on a plane surface parallel to the horizon,[6] one with great impetus, and the other more slowly. And suppose that they move in opposite directions from opposite parts and meet in the middle in an interacting motion. In that case, there is no doubt that the weaker will be thrust back by the stronger and forced to move back. But how can they say that at that point of impact an interval of rest occurs? For if once they remained at rest, they would thereafter always be at rest, since they would not have reason for moving. In the case of the large stone falling from a high point, even if it were stopped by the pebble, yet after the interval of rest, both would fall together, moving down by reason of their own weight. But when they are in a plane parallel to the horizon there exists no cause of motion after the [supposed] interval of rest.

Before expounding my last argument, I make these two assumptions. My first assumption is that only then is it possible for a body to be at rest outside its proper place, when the force that opposes its fall is equal to its weight, which exerts pressure downward. Surely this is clear: for if the impressed force 327 was greater than the resistant weight, the body would continue to move upward; and if it were smaller, the body would fall. Secondly, I assume that the same body can be sustained in the same place over equal intervals of time by equal forces.

I then urge the following. If a state of rest lasting for some interval of time occurs at the turning point, e.g., when a stone changes from forced upward motion to [natural] downward motion, then over the same interval of time there will exist equality between the projecting force and the resisting weight. But this is

6. Galileo does not enter here into the problem of the horizontal plane (301, above).

impossible, since it was proved in the previous chapter that the projecting force is continuously diminished. For the motion in which the stone changes from accidental lightness to heaviness is one and continuous, as when iron moves [i.e., changes] from heat to coldness. Therefore the stone will not be able to remain at rest.

Furthermore, suppose that the stone moves forcibly from *a* to *b,* and naturally from *b* to *a.* If, then, the stone is at rest at *b* for some interval of time, suppose that this time has as its end moments *c* and *d.* If, then, the body is at rest for time *cd,* the external projecting force will, through time *cd,* be equal to the weight of the body. But the natural weight is always the same. Therefore the [projecting] force at moment *c* is equal to that force at moment *d.* Now it is the same stone and the same place: hence the stone will be held there over equal intervals of time by equal forces. But the force at moment *c* sustains the body throughout time *cd.* Hence the force at moment *d* will sustain the same stone through an interval of time equal to interval *cd.* The body will therefore be at rest throughout twice time *cd.* But this is inconsistent: for it was assumed to be at rest only through time *cd.* Indeed, by continuing the same form of argument, we could prove that the stone would always be at rest at *b.*

But do not be confused by the argument that, if the weight and projecting force are equal at some time, then the body must be at rest for some time. For it is one thing to say that the weight of the body at some time comes to be equal to the projecting force; but it is another thing to say that it remains in this state of equality over an interval of time. This becomes clear from the following consideration. While the body is in motion, since (as has been shown) the projecting force is always being diminished, but the intrinsic weight always remains the same, it must follow that, before they arrive at a relation of equality, countless other ratios occur. Yet it is impossible for the force and the weight to remain in any of these ratios over any interval of time. For it has been proved that the projecting force never remains

328 at the same level over an interval of time, since it is always diminishing.

And so, it is true that the [projecting] force and the weight pass through ratios of, let us say, 2 to 1, 3 to 2, 4 to 3, and countless other ratios; but it is false and impossible that they should remain for any interval of time in any one of these ratios. So, too, they arrive at equality at some moment, but they do not remain at equality. This being so, since local motion upward and downward is a consequence of that alterative motion of change from light *per accidens* to heavy *per se,* in such a way that upward motion flows from an excess of impressed force, downward motion from a deficiency thereof, and rest from equality, and since this equality does not persist over an interval of time, it follows that neither does the state of rest persist.

Chapter [21]

In which, in opposition to Aristotle, it is proved that if natural motion could be extended without limit, it would not become swifter without limit.

Aristotle believed (as one can see at *De Caelo* 1.88)[1] not only that natural motion is continuously accelerated until the body reaches its proper place, but also that, if the motion could continue without limit, the weight of the body and the speed of its motion would be increased without limit. For in seeking to show that the things that move are carried toward some definite place he writes as follows: "If earth, in moving downward, did not move to a definite place, but moved without limit, its weight and speed would also be increased without limit. But weight and speed without limit cannot exist. Hence what moves downward does not move without limit." This, then, is the view of Aristotle; but we shall prove the truth of the diametrically opposite view. That is, we shall show that the speed is not increased continuously, and that even if it were, and even if the motion could be extended without limit, the body would not necessarily attain unlimited weight and instantaneous speed.[2]

As to the first point, anyone will easily be able, from what has been written above, to grasp the cause of the acceleration of natural motion at the end, and hence to understand why such acceleration must finally cease. For since the [motion of the] body is accelerated because the contrary [i.e., upward] force *329* is continuously diminishing while [in consequence] the natural weight is being attained,[3] it will stand to reason that the whole contrary force will finally be lost and the natural weight resumed, and, therefore, that acceleration will cease since its cause has been removed. Yet I would not give as a reason for saying that the whole contrary force is used up that I may happen to think it necessarily true that whatever is con-

---

1. Cf. 277a27–33. The same section is quoted in a memorandum (411.11).
2. In the sense of traversing an interval of space in less than any given time.
3. Cf. 319, above.

tinually diminished is finally destroyed. For I am not unaware that this is not necessarily true, as will be explained below. I shall merely say that the force is used up because experience seems to me to confirm this. For, in the first place, if we see something not at all heavy, e.g., a ball of wool or a feather or some such thing, falling from a height, we shall observe that it moves more slowly at the beginning, but yet a little later maintains a uniform motion. Now the reason why this appears more clearly in the case of less heavy objects is that, when these begin to move, since they have [impressed on them] an amount of contrary [i.e., upward] force equal to their own weight, and since they are themselves not very heavy, the contrary impressed force will also be small. Hence it will be used up quickly; and when it is all used up, these bodies will move with uniform motion. Now since they move slowly, it will be easier to observe the uniformity of the motion of these objects than of those that fall very swiftly. For in the case of heavier bodies, since a great deal of contrary force must be used up in the course of their fall, more time will be required for it to be used up. Now in the course of this time, since they move quickly, they will fall a great distance. And since we cannot avail ourselves of such large distances from which to let heavy bodies fall, it is not strange that a stone let fall merely from the height of a tower will be observed to be accelerated all the way to the ground. For this short distance and short time of motion are insufficient for the destruction of the whole contrary force.

The second [corroborative] experience may be taken from other alterative motions [i.e., changes] in which the opposite quality is at last completely destroyed, as, for example, when iron, after being glowing hot, becomes quite cold, and all the heat is completely destroyed. We must, therefore, think of the stone in the same way, as it changes from light to heavy, losing all its extraneous lightness. And when this happens, the increase of velocity will cease.

Thirdly, it can be confirmed by reason and experience that not only are motions not subject to continuous acceleration in the cases where the body leaves from a state of rest, but also that, if at the beginning of such motion a large force projecting the body downward is impressed on it by an external mover, this force too is used up. And the reason is that in that case the heaviness of the body would have the effect of lightness,[4] since that heaviness, un-

4. I.e., as compared with the combined effect of intrinsic heaviness and the downward impetus added from without.

adulterated and simple, would produce a slower fall than when mingled with the [downward] force. And so the characteristic and natural slowness of the [freely] falling body would oppose the force that [extraneously] impels it downward.

330   The common experience of divers and swimmers will further clarify this by way of example. For their natural weight is great enough for them to sink, if they wish, to the bottom of the sea; and in that case they will go down solely under the pull of their own weight. But if they are thrown down by an external mover, with no matter how great a force, e.g., if they are thrown from a high place, like the top of a ship's mast, at first their motion in the water will certainly be forcibly quickened and swifter than natural. But that motion will be retarded by the body's absolute natural weight: for this weight, by comparison with the combination of weight and impressed force, amounts to lightness. And the motion will be retarded until the sinking body arrives at its natural slowness. Moreover, if the water is quite deep the diver will not suffer any greater injury at the bottom than if he went down only from the surface of the water with his own natural motion.

The following argument may be elicited from these facts. If the motion of a falling body were always undergoing acceleration, that body would be capable of every speed whatever,[5] so that no speed would be unnatural for it. Hence, it would not lose and cast off the downward impetus it had received from an external mover, since it would at length have arrived naturally at that same impetus. But experience shows us that the opposite takes place. Hence it is clear to all that for a body falling in natural motion a definite and determinate [maximum] speed is fixed.[6]

But even if the speed were always increasing and the path of the motion were unlimited, still it would not follow that the motion would attain unlimited speed and the body unlimited weight. This will not be hard to understand for those who are experienced in mathematics. For it is like the proposition that seems impossible to virtually all who are incapable of following the demonstration, viz., that two lines can be found which, when

5. This proposition is contradicted by the next paragraph.

6. Marginal note: "The argument will be better formulated as follows: If the falling body is always undergoing acceleration, it will certainly be able at some time to attain a speed greater than any given speed, of which it will not rid itself. But it does rid itself of some assigned speed. It will therefore do the same with any greater speed. For let the given speed be that which is impressed by an external mover, as in this example" (F).

indefinitely produced, always approach each other but never meet, so that the distance between them always becomes smaller and smaller without end, yet never is entirely consumed. But that such lines exist is known to all who have met with the asymptotes of the hyperbola in the *Conics* of Apollonius of Perga, or with the first conchoid curve of Nicomedes in

331   the commentary of Eutocius of Ascalon on peerless Archimedes' *Sphere and Cylinder,* Book 2.[7] For these are cases of two lines (and many other cases could also be thought of) which, when extended indefinitely, always keep approaching each other, though it is impossible that they should ever meet. That is, the distance between them is always diminishing but is never completely destroyed. Thus let us suppose that a line is drawn at right angles to the straight line that lies under the conchoid, or at right angles to the asymptote [of the hyperbola], and let us suppose that this line, always remaining at right angles, moves without limit in the direction in which the nonconcurrent lines are indefinitely extended. Then the point on this perpendicular at which it is intersected by the hyperbola or the conchoid will always move toward the other end [of the perpendicular], and will approach it, but will never reach its end point.

The same argument applies to the speed [of natural motion]: for the slowness of the motion can be continually diminished (with consequent increase of the speed), and yet never be completely destroyed. For example, let *ab* be the slowness, so that if the body consumed it entirely, the motion would take place in an instant. I say that, though *ab* is being diminished always and without end, it does not follow that it is ultimately destroyed. For suppose that a motion begins which can be extended indefinitely, and suppose that by the end of the first mile it is accelerated to the extent that it destroys an eighth part of the slowness *ab,* let us say, *ac.* And suppose that by the end of the second mile it destroys an eighth part of the residual slowness, *cb;* and by the end of the next mile it destroys an eighth part of the next residuum. Now in this way this diminution can always be extended indefinitely, since the seven-eighths that remain can always be redivided into eight equal parts.[8] And the body will be able to move over miles without end, destroying something of its slowness in each and every

7. In Archimedes, *Opera,* ed. Heiberg (Leipzig, 1915), Vol. III, pp. 98–104. Pappus (Bk. IV, p. 244, Hultsch) refers, without giving details, to four forms of the conchoid of Nicomedes in each of which the "ruler" (called here by Galileo "the straight line that lies under the conchoid") is presumably asymptotic to the curve.

8. So that by the end of the next mile one of these eight parts is lost.

mile: but it does not follow that the slowness will be completely destroyed.

And, what is more, those people who with Aristotle have believed that if slowness is always being diminished, the body must reach unlimited speed—what will they say if it is shown to them not only that unlimited speed need not necessarily result, but also that a body may always undergo acceleration, without there being such an increase in speed as to equal, much less exceed, a certain finite velocity? To put it more clearly, suppose a body moves with a speed of *ab* at the beginning of its motion. Now let there be another speed *cd* greater than *ab*. I say that a body moving without end can keep on always increasing its speed, and yet that this speed, though forever growing greater, will never equal speed *cd*. This would be the case if, starting from rest, a body were to acquire, by the end of the first mile, a speed *ab*, which is two-thirds of *cd*; and if, by the end of the second mile its speed were increased by one-third of speed *ab*, by the end of the third mile by one-third of one-third of *ab*, by the end of the fourth mile, by one-third of one-third of one-third of *ab*, and if the increase in the course of each successive mile were one-third of the increase in the preceding mile, and so on without end. Surely the speed will always increase, and yet will never equal *cd*, but will always be less than *cd* by one-half the last increment.[9]

332

The proof is as follows. Consider a sequence of any number of speeds, each one three times its successor, *ab*, *bc*, and *cd*, with *ab* the largest. Let $ea = 3ab/2$. I say that the sum of all the magnitudes, *ab*, *bc*, and *cd*, increased by one-half *cd*, is equal to *ea*.

For since $ea = 3 ab/2$,
$$ab + \tfrac{1}{2} ab = ea.$$
And since $ab = 3 bc$,
$$bc + \tfrac{1}{2} bc = \tfrac{1}{2} ab.$$
But it has been shown that $ab + \tfrac{1}{2} ab = ae$.
Therefore $ac + \tfrac{1}{2} bc = ae$.
Similarly, since $bc = 3 cd$,
$$cd + \tfrac{1}{2} cd = \tfrac{1}{2} bc.$$
But $ac + \tfrac{1}{2} bc = ae$, as was shown above.
Therefore $ad + \tfrac{1}{2} dc = ae$.

9. The increase of speed is continuous, but Galileo converts the problem into an arithmetic one by considering accumulated discrete increments at the end of successive miles.

And by always repeating the same argument, it will be proved that the sum of any number of successive speeds, each one three times its successor, plus one-half the smallest, is equal to a speed three-halves that of the greatest speed of the sequence. And if this is true, clearly the sum of all the terms of a sequence of speeds, each one three times its successor, is less than a speed three-halves that of the greatest speed of the sequence, since there will always be a deficiency of one-half the smallest speed of the sequence. It is clear, therefore, that speed *ab* can be increased continuously and forever, and yet it would never equal *ae*. Let us conclude, therefore, that in the case of a [freely falling] body, for the reasons previously given, the speed does not grow indefinitely great, but that there is a certain speed beyond which its fixed weight does not permit it to move naturally.

333

But even if it were conceded that the velocity of the body underwent continuous increase forever, the velocity still would not necessarily become indefinitely great.[10]

From what has thus far been written, anyone can readily discover the reason why heavy bodies do not, in their natural motions, adhere to the ratios which we assigned to them when we discussed the matter, i.e., the ratios of the weights of the bodies in the medium through which they are moving. For, since at the beginning of their motion, they do not move in accordance with their weights, being impeded by the contrary force,[11] it will certainly not be surprising that the speeds do not adhere to the ratios of the weights. Indeed—and this surely seems remarkable—lighter bodies will fall more swiftly than heavier ones at the beginning of their motion. Now other writers, too, have tried to assign a cause for this remarkable effect. But, since they did not master the problem, we shall in the next chapter refute their explanation and shall try to set forth the true cause.

10. I.e., greater than any assigned velocity. Years later, Galileo was able to formulate the concept of terminal velocity based on resistance of the medium. In the present passage, however, the possibility of an asymptotic approach to an ultimate velocity is quite differently conceived, namely, as caused by an unending diminution of the impressed contrary force. But note that the discussion is hypothetical, and that Galileo holds that in fact the impressed contrary force is completely consumed, so that the maximum velocity of fall is actually attained and adhered to until the end of the fall,

11. See 320, above,

Chapter [22]

In which the cause is given why, at the beginning of their natural motion, bodies that are less heavy move more swiftly than heavier ones.

This problem, surely, is no less attractive than difficult. Other writers, too, have tried to explain its solution, e.g., Averroes and his followers.[1] But, in my opinion, they labored in vain laying down certain unattractive hypotheses. For they hold[2] that air is heavy in its own region, from which it follows that things which have more air are heavier in the region of air—and this is also Aristotle's opinion. Thus [they say] a wooden sphere, for example, since it has more air in it than a leaden one, has three heavy elements, air, water, and earth; while the leaden one, since it has less air in it, has, as it were, only two heavy elements: the result of this is that the wooden sphere falls [in air] more swiftly than the leaden. And not content with this, they also say that rare lead is heavier than dense iron in air for the reason that there are more parts of air in rare lead than in dense iron. No one will fail to see how many and how serious are the difficulties that this solution involves.

334   In the first place, who does not know that air is neither heavy nor light in its own region, and that, as a consequence, it moves neither upward nor downward? This was proved above.[3]

Secondly, if the velocity of the [natural] motion of a body depends on its weight, as everyone holds, and if the leaden sphere has earth and water in place of the portions of air that are in the wooden sphere, and if earth and water are heavier than air, as we can readily believe, then will not the lead be heavier and fall more swiftly? And as for what they say about iron and lead, to show that air adds to the weight, if lead is heavier because it has

---

1. Averroes does not take up this question. In comm. 29 on *De Caelo* IV to which Borri refers (p. 214 of the work cited in note 2, below), Averroes is concerned with the question why a large piece of wood is heavier in one medium (e.g., air) and lighter in another (e.g., water) than a small piece of lead.

2. Marginal note: "Borrius, part 3. ch. 12" (F). [See Hieronymus Borrius Arretinus, *De Motu Gravium et Levium* (Florence, 1576), p. 232. In part 3, ch. 7 (pp. 214–17), Borri (who taught at Pisa while Galileo was a student there) describes an experiment of throwing two equal weights of lead and wood simultaneously from his window. Seeing the wood fall faster (in repeated trials), he reasons as Galileo relates. Borri does not limit his statement to the start of the fall; his reasoning is refuted by Galileo, who asserts that the wood falls faster *only at the beginning,* and tries to explain why the lead later on overtakes the wood.]

3. Ch. 11, above.

more air, then wood will be heavier than both iron and lead, since it has more air than either of them.

Thirdly, if the great quantity of air which is in wood makes the wood move more swiftly, then it will always [and not merely in the beginning] move more swiftly, so long as it is in the air. But experience shows us the opposite. For it is true that wood moves more swiftly than lead in the beginning of its motion; but a little later the motion of the lead is so accelerated that it leaves the wood behind it. And if they are both let fall from a high tower, the lead moves far out in front. This is something I have often tested. Therefore we must try to derive a sounder explanation on the basis of sounder hypotheses.

Oh, how readily are true explanations derived from true principles! If it is true, as we said,[4] that bodies, when they begin their motion from a state of rest, begin it with an impressed force in the opposite direction equal to their weight, then the bodies that are heavier will begin their motion charged with a greater contrary force. But if heavier bodies must destroy more of the force that impels them in the opposite direction [to their natural motion] than must lighter bodies, then it surely follows that heavier bodies move more slowly since they are subject to greater resistance. And, on the other hand, if this is true, it follows that the heavier bodies must fall faster, once they have destroyed so much of the contrary resistance that they are no longer hindered by as much as the lighter bodies are. And experience again definitely confirms this.

But we must not silently pass over a great difficulty that arises at this point. For, though heavier bodies have more of the opposite quality to destroy than do lighter bodies, still they also have greater weight with which to destroy it. This being so, it seems logical that they should move merely with equal speed at the beginning: and the reason why the less heavy bodies must move more quickly is not yet clear.

335

This objection surely has great weight; but still it is not so powerful that it can obscure the brightness of the truth. And in order to overcome it, we must note that the contrary quality in a body is not destroyed because it is attacked by the weight of the body. For weight cannot accomplish this, since it is completely nonexistent in a body filled with the contrary quality; but that quality is weakened by itself and abandons the body.[5] The case

4. 320, above.
5. There is something of a contradiction with the preceding paragraph on whether the impressed force is destroyed by the natural weight of the body. But the preceding paragraph seems merely to be recording a hypothetical objection.

is like that of the glowing hot iron when it grows cold. The heat in the iron is lost not because it is resisted by the opposing cold—for there is no cold at that time in the iron—but it passes from the iron gradually by its own nature.

Secondly, we must note that the lighter the body is on which the contrary quality has been impressed, the more readily and swiftly does this quality depart. And this we may confirm by many examples. Thus, if two small balls, one of lead, the other of wood, are shot out at one and the same time from the same cannon, then, beyond any doubt, the same force will be impressed on both of them. Yet this force will be preserved more intensively and for a longer time in the lead than in the wood. An indication of this is the fact that the lead will move farther and for a longer time in the forced motion. The same thing is seen if one throws two objects, one a piece of wood and the other a piece of iron [or lead], straight upward with the same hand at one and the same time. The piece of iron or lead will move a longer distance: and this shows that the motive force inheres more strongly in the iron and is preserved there for a longer time than in the wood.[6]

And this same thing is seen if two weights, one of wood, the other of lead, are suspended, each by a cord, and then receive an impetus [by being drawn to one side] the same distance from the perpendicular. If, then, the weights are allowed to swing, the lead weight will certainly move back and forth for a longer interval of time.[7]

Finally, it is clear in all cases that all contrary qualities are preserved longer, the heavier, denser and more opposed to these qualities is the material on which they have been impressed. For if wood and lead are heated so that they are both equally hot to begin with, the heat will still be preserved longer in the lead, even though the greater coldness of the lead offers more opposition to heat than does the lesser coldness of the wood. This is clearly seen in the case of air. If air has been strongly heated by direct action of fire, then if the fire is removed or covered with ashes, the air immediately becomes cold. But if water is heated by fire, I will not say to the point of boiling, but merely so that it is as hot as the air had been, it will certainly preserve that heat for a long time—even though the coldness of water is far more hostile to heat than is the air. It is obvious,

336

---

6. The examples given here and in the next two paragraphs are also the subjects of memoranda, 410.4–7 and 413.1–6.

7. Here and in the corresponding memorandum (413.1) we have the earliest references attesting Galileo's interest in the pendulum.

too, that in the summertime iron or stones become much hotter than air (for our hands can hardly stand the heat of the stone), and preserve that heat for a long time; but in winter these same stones become far colder than the air itself. And so, from all these examples it is clear that all contrary qualities inhere more strongly in heavier and denser material and leave this material more slowly.

Now with these facts established, the solution to our problem is clear. For if contrary qualities were used up in the same ratio in wood and lead, it would be true that they would both move with the same speed at the beginning of their natural motion. But since a contrary quality is used up more readily and quickly in less heavy material, the result is that an impressed force is destroyed in wood and vanishes from it more swiftly. This being so, wood will necessarily move more swiftly. But once the contrary quality is lost, wood does not attain as much weight as does lead, since lead, unencumbered and by itself, is heavier than wood. And that is the reason why lead subsequently catches up with wood and leaves it far behind.

But these things may be still more easily clarified by an example. Suppose that there are two bodies, equal in size, one of wood, the other of lead, that the weight of the lead is 20, and of the wood 4, and that both are held up by line *ab*. Now, in the first place, it is clear that these bodies press downward with a force equal to that with which line *ab* presses upward. For if they exerted more than that pressure, line *ab* would not hold them up, but they would move downward in spite of the line. But actually those bodies do not move downward in the air because they are not exerting weight upon the air, the medium through which they must move (and, indeed, nothing moves downward, as we

have shown, unless it is heavier than the medium through which it must move). It is rather on *ab* that the bodies are exerting pressure, and since the downward pressure they exert is not greater than the upward pressure of the line, they are necessarily at rest. But when they are released by the [removal of the] line, they still retain, at the first point of their departure, an impressed contrary quality that impels them upward; and this quality is lost not instantaneously but gradually. The lead has 20 units of this contrary quality to be used up, and the wood 4. Now if this quality were uniformly used up in each body, so that, when one unit of the quality in the lead departed, one unit in the wood did likewise, and, if, as a conse-

337

quence, both of them had recovered one unit of weight, then, no doubt, both of them would move with equal speed.[8]

But in the time in which one unit of the quality departs from the lead, more than one unit has left the wood; and, as a consequence, while the lead has recovered only one unit of weight, the wood has recovered more than one. It is because of this that the wood moves more swiftly during that time. Again, in the time in which two units of the [contrary] quality depart from the wood, less than two depart from the lead. And it is because of this that the lead moves more slowly during that time. On the other hand, because the lead finally reacquires more weight than the wood, it follows that by that time the lead is moving much more swiftly.

8. But only for the first part of the fall, i.e., until four units of the contrary quality were used up by lead and wood alike. After that the lead, but not the wood, would continue to accelerate.

Chapter [23]

Why objects projected by the same force move farther on a straight line[1] the less acute are the angles they make with the plane of the horizon.[2]

Anyone might bring up this not inconsiderable difficulty on the basis of what we wrote when we discussed motion over planes inclined at various angles to the horizon. For there the conclusion is reached that the more acute the angle that the plane, over which motion takes place, makes with the horizon, the more easily will a heavy body be able to be projected up that plane.[3] But now we seem[4] to be saying the opposite. Therefore anyone might have justifiable grounds for doubting. But in order that this difficulty may be overcome, insofar as there seems to be a conflict with what was said above, we must note the following.

1. The initial part of the trajectory of a projectile is considered to be a straight line. This is the straight line here referred to and is measured from the point of projection to the point where the projectile supposedly leaves its straight path. In the dialogue version (368.19) the question is said to have been raised by Dionigius Fons (see Appendix II, note 2). Galileo, who later proved that the trajectory was parabolic, here takes what was presumably the still current view of the trajectory (straight line, curve, straight line), though Tartaglia had already (1546) suggested a trajectory that was continuously curved.

Note that, while the previous discussion had dealt with the case of vertical projection, only here does Galileo specifically take up the nonvertical case, and the result is far from satisfactory.

2. I.e., the nearer the angle of projection is to 90°.

3. See above, 298.

4. Reading *videamur* (337.18).

When we said above that heavy bodies move up [an inclined plane] more easily, according as the plane, over which the motion takes place, is more inclined [away from the perpendicular], the statement is to be understood of bodies which move on a solid plane. But the present statement is about bodies that are not supported by some other [solid], but are driven upward and sustained aloft in the air merely by impressed force. This is the case, for example, when iron balls are shot from cannons used for battering walls. Surely it is clear that they move over a longer path in the same straight line, according as the line of motion makes less acute angles with the horizon.

In order that we may find the true cause of this effect, whatever others may say, we must observe, as we also noted above, that an impelling force is impressed far more strongly on that which resists it more, provided that the force does not fail through weakness. And if we could find some reason why the

338 same heavy body offers more resistance [to an impressed force] now than at some previous time, then it will doubtless be now that the body is more strongly moved by the force. But that which presses forward in opposition to a force offers more resistance to it than that which either is at rest or moves in the same direction [as the force]. Hence the force is more strongly impressed on a body which presses forward against it.

Those who play ball know this by experience. They want the ball thrown hard toward them, so that [in hitting it back] they may impress more motive force upon it, as it actively opposes and resists [that force]. But, as we have already said, only those can accomplish this who have a strong and vigorous arm. Those who are weak and who cannot exert force against the force [of the oncoming ball] strike the ball when it is at rest or at least not moving toward them; and if the ball is moving in the same direction [as the direction in which they are to hit it] only a little force can be imparted to it [by the blow], as everyone knows. And the cause of this effect is that, when a body at rest is struck with a great force, it moves before the entire force is impressed on it: for, because of its readiness to move, it does not wait for so large a force to be impressed on it. But this does not take place in the case of a body which is moving in the direction opposite [that of the force to be impressed]: for since its resistance is increased by the movement of its weight, it resists the force more, and does not reverse its direction before all the force has been impressed on it.

We all experience this when we wish to throw a stone forward.

For we first swiftly carry it back in our hand, so that, having thus been moved in the opposite direction, not only the stone but also the hand may offer greater resistance to the impressing of the force. But if, after the stone has been carried back, we stopped moving our hand and the stone came to rest after having thus moved back, the distance it could be thrown would be much smaller. This is clear to everyone. And so, for the throw to have greater power, the stone, after being carried back, must not come to rest at the turning point. The same thing is obvious in the case of those who cast a stone with a sling. For they first whirl the sling around two or three times in a circle so that it may move more quickly, and finally they change this motion to a backward one, so that a greater force may then be impressed on the actively resisting stone.

On the basis of these observations, I give a twofold explanation of the problem under discussion. First I say that though the motive force remains the same in the cannon, yet more of the force is impressed on the iron ball, the more erect the cannon stands.[5] And the reason for this is that the ball then resists the force more. For it is less ready to move from the ball chamber when it is to be fired upward in a more elevated direction than when the line of fire is lower. Hence it offers greater resistance to the impressing of force upon it. For when the cannon is aimed almost horizontally, the ball does not wait for the impressing of force to be completed, but is shot out before that im-
339   pressing is completed. On the other hand, when the cannon is aimed vertically upward, the ball presses down on the gunpowder with its weight and offers more resistance to vertical upward motion, and awaits the impressing of a large amount of force before departing.[6]

And we need not have any fears that the projecting force may prove weak and inadequate. For this force is so great that, if the ball is so tightly squeezed in the ball chamber that it cannot be shot out, the whole cannon will be blown to bits. For such a mass of fire compressed in so narrow a space would destroy not only those bronze chambers, but chambers even a hundred times stronger. This is obvious since it blows walls, ramparts, and whole fortifications sky-high. How great a mass of fire is enclosed

5. I.e., the nearer the angle of projection is to 90°.
6. Cf. the memorandum (411.28): "Light bodies are not moved more swiftly by a greater force. Just as straw and tow are not heated any more by the greatest and strongest fire, because they do not wait for such heat, but are burned sooner by the smaller degree of heat, so light bodies do not wait for a great force to be impressed on them, but are moved before then."

at that time in the narrow chamber, may be judged from the amount of gunpowder, which sometimes comes to eight or ten pounds in weight and is entirely converted into fire, leaving practically no ashes or other residues from the fire. And how great is the volume of fire whose weight comes to ten pounds should be pondered especially by those who suppose that there is no weight in fire. So much for the first explanation.

The second explanation is as follows. When a ball is sent up perpendicularly to the horizon, it cannot turn from that course and make its way back over the same straight line, as it must, unless the quality that impels it upward has first disappeared entirely.[7] But this does not happen when the ball is sent up on a line inclined to the horizon. For in that case it is not necessary for the [impressed] projecting force to be entirely used up when the ball begins to be deflected from the straight line. For it is enough that the impetus that impels the body by force keeps it from [returning to] its original point of departure. And this it can accomplish so long as the body moves on a line inclined to the horizon, even though it may be only a little inclined [from the perpendicular] in its motion. For at the time when the ball begins to turn down [from the straight line], its motion is not contrary to the [original] motion in a straight line; and, therefore, the body can change over to the [new] motion without the complete disappearance of the impelling force. But this cannot happen while the body is moving perpendicularly upward, because the line of the downward path is the same as the line of the forced motion. Therefore, whenever in its downward course, the body does not move toward the place from which it was projected by the impressed force, that force permits it to turn downward.[8] For it is sufficient for that force that it keeps the body from returning to the point from which it departed.

And the force will the more readily permit the body to turn down, the less that downturn will interfere with the length of the interval from the starting place. But if the motion is along the perpendicular *ab,* the body is in no way able to turn down away from that path, unless, by moving back along the same line, it moves toward the terminus from which it originally started. But the projecting force will never, so long as it is alive,

7. This contradicts the statement made previously (e.g., 319), that at the highest point of the vertical motion the impressed force is not zero, but is equal to the weight.

8. I.e., the body may turn downward, even though the process of diminution of the impressed force has not gone as far as would be necessary to permit a turning down after vertical upward projection.

permit this. On the other hand, when the body moves over line *ac,* since the line of downward motion is still not very far from the terminus from which the body was projected, the force of projection will not permit this downturn unless it has been very largely weakened. But when the body moves alone *ae,* which is almost parallel to the horizon, the body can begin to turn downward almost immediately. For this turning down does not interfere with distance [measured along the ground] from the starting point.

But the opposite of this takes place when the body moves up on various inclined planes. For in the case of the planes more inclined [away from the perpendicular], the body is moved farther on a straight line by the same force than in the case of planes more nearly perpendicular. And the reason for this is that the more the plane is inclined [away from the perpendicular] the less heavy[9] is the body there, because part of its weight is sustained by the plane. Hence it can be more readily moved by the mover. And since, on these planes, the body cannot turn downward except by moving back over the same straight line, a body will move farther in a straight line on those planes on which the weight[10] of that body is less.

9. The component of weight parallel to the plane is referred to.
10. See the previous note.

Appendix I

The Reworkings of Parts of the De Motu

As was noted in the Introduction, Galileo reworked at least
parts of the material that Favaro presented as the first version of
the *De Motu*. Thus there are two sheets among Galileo's manuscripts which contain another version of Chapters 1 and 2. This
version is published by Favaro on pp. 341–43 of his edition; I
refer to it hereafter as version II. There are also 18 sheets which
contain reworkings of the whole or parts of chapters 1–6 and 12.
This material is published by Favaro on pp. 344–66; I refer to it
hereafter as version III.

I have not thought it necessary to translate versions II and III
in full, since in considerable measure they repeat what Favaro
published as the first version (referred to hereafter as version I).
But there are some things worth mentioning.

Versions II and III emphasize more than does version I the
relativity of "down" and "up" and propose the use of the terms
"nearer the center" and "farther from the center." And the later
versions also avoid the word "light," substituting "less heavy."
They emphasize (even more than does version I) the meaning-
lessness of terms like "absolutely heavy" and "absolutely light"
and stress the idea that every upward motion is "forced."

Thus, chapter 2 in version II begins as follows (342.1–10):

*That heavier bodies are by nature located nearer the center,
and less heavy farther from the center, and why.*

Up to now we have spoken of "the heavy and the less heavy"
not of "the heavy and the light"; and of "nearer the center and
farther from the center," not of "downward and upward." We

are going to explain later on that there is nothing light, i.e., devoid of weight, and no place that is only up and not also down. Yet, if at times, out of a desire to use ordinary language (for quibbling about words has no relevance to our purpose), we speak of "the heavy and the light," and of "downward and upward," these expressions should be understood as meaning "more and less heavy" and "nearer the center and farther from the center."

Version III uses the same title for chapter 2 as does version II, but begins the chapter quite differently, as follows (344.3–18):

After the marvelous construction of the vast celestial sphere, the divine Creator pushed the refuse that remained into the center of that very sphere and hid it there. His purpose was to keep that refuse from impinging on the sight of the immortal and blessed spirits. But this dense and heavy matter did not with its own mass fill up the broad and spacious region that was left under the curved surface of the last sphere. And therefore, in order that this great region might not be unused and unoccupied, he tore apart that heavy, confused mass which, compressed by its own weight, he had shut up in narrow confines. And out of its countless particles, thinned out in greater or lesser degree, he formed those four bodies which we later called elements. The heaviest and densest of these remained in its earlier state; and he did not remove it from the place where it had previously taken refuge. Thus earth was left in the center. And similarly the denser bodies were placed nearer earth. And of the bodies that were formed from this matter those were called denser which contained more particles of this matter in the same volume. And the denser bodies were the heavier.

Version III also has the following paragraph (346.8–17) in which the question of equal quantity of the various elements is taken up (cf. 253):

From this it may be gathered that no importance can be attached to the argument of Aristotle in which he tries to prove that the bodies of matter that make up the various elements are equal to each other. Aristotle argues that, if the igneous matter exceeded that of air and of water, all the air and water would have been burned by the fire and changed into fire.[1] For even if we assume that the quantity of fire exceeds that of air a thousand times, still we need not fear that the air can be changed to the nature of fire. For since all the space underneath the sphere of

1. Marginal note: "Meteorologica 1 ch. 3" (F) [cf. 340a1 ff.].

the moon has already been filled, and if the air became fire it would require a far more extensive space than it now occupies, it is clear that the air cannot assume an igneous nature for the reason that it would lack the space in which to stay. And a similar proposition holds for the other elements.

Version III also elaborates the point that upward motion must be "forced," in a chapter entitled "That no upward motion is natural" (352–55). I quote a small portion (354.3–12):

But while we are denying naturalness to upward motion, let us consider how appropriately naturalness befits downward motion. For in downward motion there is a terminus, namely the center, from which a body cannot recede in the course of the same kind of motion as that in which the body had approached the center. For it had approached the center in downward motion; and if it is to withdraw from the center, it will have to move upward. Distance away from the center is unbounded and without end; but proximity thereto is limited, namely by the center itself. If, then, something is endowed with the property of receding from the center, surely such a body will be suited to move endlessly. But what could be more absurd than this? In accordance with reason, therefore, we shall say that motion toward the center is natural, and motion away from the center contrary to nature.

Galileo's main argument is that all bodies have weight, that is, they have an internal cause for downward motion, but no internal cause of upward motion. This is developed in a chapter entitled "That contrary to Aristotle's view, no body is without weight" (355–61)—where the Aristotelian view of the absolutely heavy and the absolutely light is combated at greater length than in version I. I quote a marginal addition (to 360.10):

Another argument can be drawn from speed of motion. For according to Aristotle himself speed is a consequence of heaviness and lightness, so that the heavier a body is the more swiftly it will fall, and the lighter it is, the more swiftly it will rise. And therefore [on Aristotle's assumption] the absolutely heaviest body, whose heaviness is such that none greater exists, will have to move with absolutely greatest speed, a speed such that none greater would be possible. And we should have to draw the same conclusion about the light. But neither Aristotle nor truth admits the possibility of motion so swift that it lacks all slowness; for such motion would be instantaneous. Therefore it is clearly absurd to posit an [absolutely] greatest lightness or heaviness. For just as, when any speed, however great, is assumed, another speed greater than it can be assigned; so, when any heaviness or lightness, however great, is assumed, another greater than it can be assigned.

And Galileo terminates the reworked chapter in the same vein as chapter 12 of version I, but with this reference to the constitution of matter (360.11–15):

Let us conclude, therefore, that no body is devoid of weight, but that all bodies are heavy, some more, some less, according as their matter is more crowded together and compressed, or diffused and spread out. It follows from this that we cannot say that fire is absolutely light, that is, that it lacks all heaviness; for this is a property of the void.

Also where version I speaks of the possibility of substances lighter than fire, "Vapors which rise above fire" (294.2), version III indicates that the author is thinking of comets (360.28):

But if comets are burning vapors, as the Peripatetics themselves assert, then it is certain that these vapors must have flown forth above fire. For some comets have been observed far higher than the farthest region of air which these Peripatetics posit.

In version I (259 *med.*) Galileo had shown that from one point of view the motion of freely falling or freely rising bodies in a medium, traditionally called "natural motion," could also be considered as "forced motion." In the last two chapters of version III (361–66) he develops further the argument that free fall should alone be called "natural" while all upward motion is "forced." I give these chapters in full.

361.6   *Proof that upward motion cannot, on the part*
          of the moving body, be natural.

No one can doubt that, on the part of the moving body, upward motion cannot be natural in all those cases where there is a visible external cause, as when a stone forcibly projected moves upward in air. For clearly such a motion is not natural, since it does not tend towards a goal where the body may be at rest. In fact, the body immediately changes over by itself to the downward motion that is proper to it. And so, the problem has to do with that upward motion when the body moves toward a goal where it is at rest, e.g., when wood or air moves upward in water, or fire in air. And, though it is against the view of all the Peripatetics, we have decided, on the subject of this motion, that we should say that it cannot truly be called natural. We previously corroborated this conclusion, so far as we could, with regard to the motion itself, apart from any consideration of the body or the medium. We shall try now similarly to confirm it with regard to the moving body itself.

First, then, a body cannot be said to move naturally which does not have an internal cause of its motion, but requires an external cause. But such is the case with all bodies that move upward. Therefore this motion is contrary to nature. The major premise is obvious: for that which is moved *per accidens,* by reason of some external cause, is moved by something else and not by its own nature. The minor premise is also obvious: for since every body has an internal cause of downward motion, namely heaviness, it is impossible that it also have the contrary cause of the contrary motion. And you cannot say that, just as the excess of the weight of the body over the weight of the medium is the internal cause *per se* of downward motion, so the deficiency of the weight of the body, in comparison with the weight of the medium is the internal cause *per se* of upward motion. For the absolute weight of the moving body is the cause *per se* of downward motion; and it is only *per accidens* that the aforesaid weight must exceed the weight of the medium, as it is also *per accidens* that the body moves downward in a medium that has some weight. For even if a medium had no weight and the weight of a heavy body did not therefore exceed the weight of the medium,[2] that heavy body would still move downward, because it has an internal cause of downward motion. But we cannot make the corresponding judgment about a deficiency of weight. For since deficiency of weight, namely nonheaviness, is itself nothing, a medium heavier than the body itself is of necessity required, for the body to be called deficient [in comparison with the medium] in weight. Since, then, the body cannot be nonheavy unless there is present a heavier medium—for no body is without weight by itself—it follows that the nonheaviness of the body is entirely a consequence of the heaviness of the medium. For if a heavy medium is not present, the body will no longer be nonheavy, but will thereafter be heavy. This being the case, that very nonheaviness will be external to the body, coming as it does from something else and requiring an external heaviness. Hence, if that nonheaviness is the cause of upward motion, it will be external and will come to the body from something else. And since the body does not have an internal cause for this motion, it will be impossible for the motion to be in accordance with nature.

And so, there is a difference between upward and downward

362

---

2. A sophism, which would be obvious on assigning a weight zero to the medium.

motion. For in downward motion the body does not need a medium from which to receive a cause of motion, since it has its internal weight as the cause of its downward motion. In fact, its motion is interfered with by the medium, since its weight is diminished by the medium, as will be shown below. But the cause of upward motion is dependent on a heavy medium to such an extent that in a nonheavy medium nothing at all could possibly move upward, since the nonheaviness of the body comes entirely from the heaviness of the medium.[3]

But why do we need further arguments? There is a single matter in all bodies, and it is heavy in all of them. But that same weight cannot possess natural inclinations that are contrary. Therefore, if there is one natural inclination, the opposite must be contrary to nature. But the natural inclination of weight is toward the center. Therefore it follows that the inclination away from the center is contrary to nature.

Now I can well believe that the error of those who held that motion away from the center was natural originated in their inability to discover the external cause by which the bodies were moved; and that therefore they perforce assumed that it was internal and called it lightness. Hence, in order to root out any error of this kind, let us hasten to make clear that bodies moving upward move because of an external cause, namely, by the extruding action of the medium itself.

363

Bodies previously said to move naturally upward do not so move because of an internal, but because of an external cause, namely, by the extruding action of the medium itself.

If, then, the motion of bodies moving upward is contrary to nature, they must have an external cause of their own motion. And we hold that this cause is the extruding action of the medium, which comes about as follows:

First, then, bodies moving upward must be less heavy than the medium through which they move. For it has been shown that those bodies which are heavier than some medium move downward in that medium; and those which are equally heavy move neither upward nor downward, but remain at rest in it. Hence it necessarily follows that bodies which move upward must be less heavy [than the medium]. And so, when some body less heavy

---

3. Deleted at this point: "This proposition is corroborated. For the cause of a positive effect must be positive. And upward motion is a positive effect, while nonheaviness, or, if you prefer, a deficiency of weight, i.e., lightness, is, as it were, a negation" (F). The same point is made in a memorandum, 416.4. With the paragraph as it stands cf. the memorandum, 415.32.

than a given medium is submerged in that medium, the parts of the medium that surround the body, by pressing on it with their weight, try to drive out the body from below so that they may themselves occupy the lower positions. And if the resistance they encounter in that body is less than the force which they themselves exert, they overcome the body and thrust it out. But the resistance exerted by the body against being raised will be less whenever its weight is less than the weight of the medium that presses it. In that case, then, it will be thrust out.

But in order that the whole matter may be better understood, let us give an example. Thus, consider a body *a* which is lighter than the medium, let us say, water. And suppose that the surface of the water, before body *a* is submerged in it, is along line *bc;* but that when *a* is submerged the surface of the water is raised to *de*. Clearly, then, if body *a* could not be held there, water *dc* would move down into its [original] position. That is, water *dc* exerts pressure with its weight, trying to drive out body *a* so that it [the water] may itself occupy the lower position. And *a* with its weight resists being lifted. But if the weight of water *dc* is greater than the weight of *a*, it will overcome and drive out *a*. And since the volume of water *dc* is equal to the volume of *a*, and *a* is assumed to be less heavy than water, the weight of water *dc* will be greater than that of body *a*. Hence *a* will be thrust out and driven upward by the water.

364

This is the manner in which a medium can press out and thrust out bodies that are less heavy than itself. But certain objections may be raised against what we have said. And so, we shall state these objections so that the truth of what we have said may appear more clearly from the answers to these objections.

First, then, if things are as we say, why is a mass of lead not thrust from the depths of the sea, since the sea is far heavier than the piece of lead? To this I reply: "For the piece of lead to be thrust from the sea, it is necessary that a volume of water equal to the volume of the lead be heavier than the lead. For the portion of water that can push the lead out can only be that whose place the lead occupies. And, it is this portion which, by pushing out [the lead], can enter into the place vacated by the lead. For the water which suffered an injustice at the hands of the lead, so long as its place was occupied by the lead, has only a volume equal to the volume of the lead. And it is only this water which, by pushing out [the lead], can enter into the place vacated by the lead. But if the weight of this water does not exceed the weight of the lead, it surely will not be able to raise the lead. And, in fact, the assumption is that the lead is heavier; it is, therefore, no wonder that the lead is not pushed out. But if the body had been less heavy than water, for example, if you consider a wooden sphere at the bottom of a well filled with water, the parts of the water flowing about the sphere will press upon it and will try to enter the place where the sphere now is. Yet only so much of the water will try as can be held in the space vacated by the sphere when it ascends: and this is the volume of the sphere. But if the resistance in the sphere which the water meets as it presses upon it is less than the force with which it [i.e., the water] exerts this pressure—and this will be the case whenever the sphere is less heavy than the water—then, doubtless, the water will push out and extrude the sphere."

Secondly, you will object that, if the elements do not have weight in their own region (as I asserted above that I would prove), then a heavy body will not be able to be thrust out by the weight of the medium. My answer is that it is one thing to say that elements do not have weight in their own region, and another thing to say that they are not able to exert weight. The first is false: for the weight of the same bodies is always the same. But the second is true: for heavy bodies cannot always exert their weight. This is obvious in the case of wood, which always has weight, but, if placed in water, cannot then exert weight, i.e., sink, being prevented by the greater weight of the water. Thus elements cannot exert weight in their own region inasmuch as no portion of an element [in its own region] can move downward, since the place into which it would have to move is [e.g., in the case of water] already occupied by other water, which is no less heavy than the upper portion. And although the upper portions press upon the lower, still they do not thrust them out, because they [the lower] resist with as much weight as is exerted upon them. But the case is otherwise if there is another body in the water less heavy than water. For in that case a volume of water equal to the place occupied by the body, being heavier than the body, will actually be outside its own region so long as it is above the body. (For only those bodies are in their own region which are not above less heavy bodies since, as has been said, nature has so ordered it that the heavier remain at rest under the less heavy.) Hence [the water], by exerting its own weight and encountering a lesser weight, and consequently a lesser resistance, in the [immersed] body, will push and drive out that body in the manner already explained.

Thirdly, you will raise this objection (with Aristotle *De Caelo* 1.89)[4]: "Bodies which move by being extruded are moved by force. And bodies which are moved by force, move more slowly at the end of their motion. If, then, bodies which move upward move by extrusion, they should move more slowly at the end. But

365

4. Cf. 227b1–8.

that is not the case." My answer is that the necessity of moving more slowly at the end holds not for all bodies that are moved by force, but only for those that are moved by force having already been separated from that which projected them. For example, if someone projects a stone upward, the speed of its motion is diminished toward the end, after it has been removed and separated from the projector.[5] But if the projector did not permit the body to leave his hand, it could move more swiftly even at the end. And bodies moving upward by extrusion are not separated from the motive force during their motion, but are always joined to the projector. Hence it is not necessary that their speed be diminished toward the end. You will answer: *366* "Though the speed is not diminished, yet it should not increase. Yet bodies moving upward, as fire, do move more swiftly at the end." To this I reply that the assumption [made by the objectors] that the speed of upward motion is increased, is false. For that speed is always uniform. And I cannot understand how Aristotle could have observed that bodies moving upward move more swiftly at the end.

5. Marginal addition: "And we see that the speed of bodies moving upward, when they begin to be separated from the extruding medium, is diminished; as when a piece of wood, rising in water, begins to emerge from the water" (F).

Appendix II

The Dialogue De Motu

The dialogue version referred to in the Introduction (p. 4, above) basically sets forth the same doctrine of motion as is found in the essay.

The similarities of ideas, extending to practically verbatim reproduction of long passages (e.g., 388.14–389.5 = 288.18–289.6; 391.6–392.7 = 327.12–328.4; 408.20–35 = 329.34–330.10) are evidence that both dialogue and essay were written at the same period of Galileo's life, presumably the period when he was teaching at Pisa. In the absence of definitive publication, the precise dating is uncertain.

It has been assumed (e.g., by L. Olschki, *Galilei und seine Zeit,* p. 203) that after writing the essay, Galileo composed the dialogue in order to give his ideas a more artistic and persuasive literary form, one which might appeal to a wider audience. Certainly a predilection for the dialogue form remained with him throughout life. But the evidence on the question of priority between essay and dialogue has never been set forth, and it may

well be that the dialogue version was actually begun first and then
abandoned for the essay form, or possibly that Galileo worked on
the essay and the dialogue at the same time, turning from one to
the other.[1]

Whatever may be the priority as between the dialogue and the
early form of the essay, the reworked portions of the essay (versions II and III, as described above) seem to be subsequent to the
composition of the dialogue. The dialogue (e.g., 378) adheres to
the terms *levis* and *levitas,* where the reworked portions would
prefer *minus gravis* and *minor gravitas.* And the dialogue speaks
of the upward motion of a body in a lighter medium as "natural"
(e.g., 368.8), a usage criticized by version III (352 ff.). On the
other hand, the dialogue is certainly subsequent to the construction of the *Bilancetta* (cf. p. 379), the essay on which dates from
1586 (so Favaro, E.N., I, 211).

The dialogue is between Dominicus and Alexander, the latter
representing Galileo. Dominicus indicates a desire to know Alexander's opinion on six questions (368.5 ff.):

(1) Whether you believe it true that at the turning point of
motion there must be an [interval of] rest. [Cf. ch. 20 of the
essay.]

(2) What reason you give for the fact that if two bodies of the
same size, one, let us say, of wood, the other of iron, that is, one
heavier than the other, are let fall from a height at the same moment, the wooden one moves through the air more swiftly than
the iron one, that is, the lighter more swiftly than the heavier—
if, indeed, you admit this is a fact. [Cf. beginning of ch. 22 of the
essay.]

(3) How it happens that natural motion is swifter at the end
than at the middle or at the beginning, while forced motion is

1. I have dealt with the question of priority and with other problems bearing
on the dialogue, essay, and memoranda in an article "A Note on Galileo's
De Motu."

The references to the *bilancetta* (379.28) and to Font (368.19) help to date
the dialogue. A later addition (375.10–378.3) to the dialogue, from its position
among the memoranda (cf. 409), seems to have been written before chapter 13
of the essay (see 412.10). The marginal note (to 300.13) on "neutral" motion is
probably subsequent to the references in the dialogue (e.g., 373.5, 9) to "mixed"
motion. The absence from the dialogue of any discussion of the inclined plane,
despite the extensive discussion in the essay (296–302), raises a similar presump-
tion that the dialogue is earlier. A comparison of the language of *almost* identical
passages in the essay and the dialogue, where copying from one to the other
may be assumed, tends to reinforce the conclusion that the dialogue may be the
earlier of the two works, which are admittedly very closely related in time and in
thought. (For an opposing view see E. Wohlwill, *Galilei und sein Kampf für die
Copernicanische Lehre,* I, 111–13.)

swifter at the beginning than at the middle, and swifter at the middle than at the end. [Cf. ch. 19 of the essay.]

(4) Why the same body falls more swiftly in air than in water; why, indeed, some bodies fall in air which do not sink in water. [Cf. ch. 1–6 of the essay.]

(5) (A query of our dear friend Dionigius Fons,[2] most worthy knight) What reason you give for the fact that cannons used against fortifications as well as manual arms shoot lead balls farther along a straight line if they shoot them at right angles to the horizon than if on a line parallel to the horizon, although, in the former case, the motion is more opposed to natural motion. [Cf. ch. 23 of the essay.]

(6) Why those same guns shoot heavier balls more swiftly and farther than lighter ones (e.g., iron as compared with wood), although the lighter are less resistant to an impelling force. [Cf. p. 335 of the essay.]

As I have indicated, all these questions (along with many more) are treated in the essay, but the second, fifth, and sixth are left entirely untreated in the dialogue (evidence of incompleteness?). Actually, the topics developed in the dialogue are as follows (the page references are to Favaro's edition):

370–74. Projectile motion. Refutation of the Peripatetic view that the medium supports this motion when the projector is no longer in contact with the projectile. Argument for the theory of impressed force. [Cf. ch. 17 of the essay.]

The argument concludes (373.32): "For all the reasons that have been adduced, it seems to be quite clear that the medium not only does not help the motion but rather, on the contrary, opposes it. We must conclude, therefore, that a body which moves with other than natural motion is moved by a force impressed on it by a mover. But what that force is is hidden from our knowledge."[3]

374. In connection with natural motion, the question is raised why nature has so arranged it that heavier substances are at rest under lighter. It is noteworthy that before giving a summary of the same answer as is given in the essay (ch. 2), Alexander says (18–24): "To give a reason for this order of things cannot con-

2. Identified by Favaro (E.N., XX, 442) with Dionisio Font (died Dec. 5, 1590).
3. The following was added but then deleted: "And in the same way what force it is that causes strings to resound is also hidden from our knowledge" (F). [Compare the emphasis placed on the analogies of heat and sound in the essay, ch. 17.]

tribute anything to our discussion, since it is clear that those are the facts. And to give the precise cause would, no doubt, be very difficult. Indeed, I could give no other cause save that things had to be disposed in some order, and it has pleased nature to dispose them in this order.[4] Unless, perchance, we should wish to say that the heavier bodies are nearer to the center than the lighter, because, somehow, those bodies seem to be heavier which contain more matter in a smaller space ...."

375–78. In opposition to the idea of the absolutely heavy and the absolutely light. [Cf. ch. 12 of the essay.]

378–84. Relative heaviness and lightness in terms of relative density. The natural motion of a body in a fluid medium as based on the laws of hydrostatics, with speed dependent on the difference between the density of the body and the medium. [Cf. ch. 1, 3–6, 8 of the essay.]

385–88. Cf. ch. 11 of the essay.

386.25–32 affords a concise statement (cf. ch. 12 of the essay): "*Alexander*. If we speak of absolute weight and lightness, I say that all bodies, whether they are mixtures or not, have weight. But if we speak of relative weight and lightness, I say again that all bodies have weight, but some more and some less, and that it is this lesser weight which we call lightness. And so we say that fire is lighter than air, not because it lacks weight, but because it has less weight than air; and we say, in the same way, that air is lighter than water."

390–93. That there is no interval of rest at the turning point between upward and downward motion. [Cf. ch. 20 of the essay.]

394–97. That motion in a void would not necessarily be instantaneous. This is a consequence of the proposition (maintained in opposition to Aristotle) that the velocity of the natural motion of a body in a medium is proportional to the *difference* in density between the body and the medium. [Cf. ch. 13 of the essay.]

398–404. Further discussion of the speed of natural motion. [Cf. ch. 8 of the essay.]

405–6. Cf. ch. 21 of the essay. The dialogue concludes with a discussion of the acceleration of freely falling bodies. It is indicated that a body, at the start of a free fall (or at the highest point reached after vertical upward projection), has impressed on it an upward force equal to the weight of the body, and that ac-

---

4. Marginal note: "And this is the reason given by Aristotle, *Phys.* 8.32." Cf. the different attitude in the essay (p. 252 F and version III [Appendix I]).

celeration is the effect produced by the gradual dissipation of this impressed force. The question is raised whether this force is completely used up so that acceleration comes to an end. I quote a portion of the dialogue (406.26–408.20) because of material it contains that is not in the essay, e.g., an argument that what sometimes appears to be acceleration is an optical illusion:

Dominicus. What you say is quite convincing. But there still is something that troubles my mind. For if the slowness of natural motion at the beginning comes about from the resistance of the impressed force, that force will ultimately be consumed, since you assert that it is continuously diminished. And, therefore, once that force has become nil, the natural motion will not be further accelerated. But this is contrary to the view of many.

Alexander. The fact that it is contrary to the view of many does not concern me, so long as it is in harmony with reason and experience, even though at times experience seems rather to point to the opposite. For if a stone falls from a high tower,[5] its speed is observed always to be increasing. But this happens because the stone is very heavy in comparison with the medium through which it moves, i.e., the air. Since it starts its fall with an impressed force equal to its weight, it starts, of course, with much impressed force; and the motion from the height of the tower is insufficient for the using up of all this impressed force. Thus it happens that the speed continues to increase all through the distance of the single tower. But if we were to take an object that had weight, but whose weight did not so very far exceed the weight of air, we should then surely see with our own eyes that, a little after the beginning of its motion, the body would move uniformly, so long as the air remained quite calm. And we would observe the same thing happen in the case of the stone, if it were dropped from very high places and we were so placed as always to observe the line of motion under the same conditions.[6] For our position, too, keeps us from observing the uniformity of the motion.

 Thus, suppose that there is a uniform motion from *b* to *f*, and that distances *bc, cd, de,* and *ef* are equal. Let the eye of the observer be at *a*, and draw the lines of sight, *ab, ac, ad, ae,* and *af*. Since the motion is assumed to be uniform, and distances *bc, cd, de,* and *ef* are equal, the body will traverse these distances in equal times. Thus the time of transit from *b* to *c* will be the same as that from *c* to *d*. But the motion from *c* to *d* will appear swifter

 5. Cf. 329, above.
 6. I.e., so that equal distances on that line subtended equal angles in the eye of the observer.

to the observer, since distance *cd* appears greater than distance *bc;* for it is seen under a greater angle.[7] So, too, the motion from *d* to *e* will appear swifter than that from *c* to *d,* since distance *de* appears greater than distance *cd,* but is traversed by the body in equal time. Similarly, the motion from *e* to *f* will appear swifter than that from *d* to *e.* Hence also the whole motion from *b* to *f* will appear not to be uniform, but to be always accelerated to the very end, although it is assumed to be uniform.

Hence, in order to distinguish between accelerated motion and uniform motion, the distance must be great enough for the body to be able in the course of it to use up the entire [impressed] force that resists [the downward motion], and the observer's eye must be so placed as not to be deceived by the disparity of angles.

Do. I fully understand your very elegant explanation. And so, I have but one further question to ask on this subject—that is, whether, in your opinion, a heavy body that is projected downward with some force by a mover is accelerated in its
408   motion in the same way as a heavy body which, as it begins to fall, has received from a mover no force impelling it downward.[8]

Al. From what has been set forth above it is clear that a heavy body falling from a state of rest undergoes acceleration up to the point where the impressed force that resists [the downward motion] is completely consumed. But if that force is destroyed by an external mover, the body will then not undergo further acceleration.

If, for example, a body with a weight of 4 falls from a state of rest, it will, of course, start with a resistance of 4. Since this resistance has to be destroyed by the weight of the body, the natural motion will be slower at the beginning. But if the aforesaid [impressed] force of 4 is destroyed by an external mover which impresses on the body a downward pressing force of 4, then surely the body's motion will no longer be accelerated, since at the very beginning it is not retarded by any force resisting [the downward motion].

But if the force of downward projection impressed on the body by the external mover is less than 4, i.e., less than the [contrary] force which was impressed on the body while it was at rest, then surely the body will be accelerated [in its downward motion]. For some portion of the contrary force will still have to be consumed, since it was not entirely destroyed by the external mover.

And if the force of downward projection impressed on the body is greater than 4, then the natural motion will be swifter at the beginning [than subsequently], for it will then be moving

7. I.e., *cd* subtends a greater angle in the eye of the observer than does *bc.*
8. Compare what follows with the discussion in the essay (329.30 ff.).

with greater than natural speed, one that exceeds the speed required by its characteristic weight.[9]

[There follows (408.20–35), with only slight differences, the equivalent of 329.34–330.13 of the essay, and the dialogue ends at that point, with the example of the swimmer.]

9. I.e., its speed at the beginning is greater than the greatest speed a body of its specific gravity could ever attain in that medium in a free fall from rest.

Appendix III

The Memoranda on Motion

Among Galileo's early manuscripts on motion is the series of notes and memoranda referred to in the Introduction and published on pages 409–19 of Favaro's edition.

These memoranda are interesting for they show what Galileo in his reading and reflection considered worth noting. While we cannot precisely date the papers, their content is very closely connected with that of the essay and dialogue on motion. We may therefore presume that they were made in preparation for these writings and in the course of their composition and revision, probably in the years when Galileo was teaching at Pisa. We may also note that the later pages of notes (414–17) are largely concerned with a chief point of the last rewriting (what we have called version III) of the essay, the impossibility of upward natural motion. What seems to be a plan or program of a work on motion (418–19) does not really continue the memoranda (409–17); it appears to have been written earlier, perhaps before the first version of the essay, and is actually on a sheet separate from the other notes and is preserved separately from them.

Galileo incorporates in his essay on motion the substance of most of these memoranda, sometimes verbatim. I have referred to instances of special interest in my notes to the translation of the essay. But there are some additional points that may be noted here.

One memorandum speaks of a chapter that must be written (412.10: the chapter is ch. 13 of the essay). In another (412.19) he predicts what the public reaction to his writings will be: "There will be many who, after reading my writings, will turn their mind not to consider whether what I have said is true, but merely to seek means of impugning my arguments, whether justly or unjustly."

These memoranda bear on the question of dating; and if the

reference in the latter one is to the writings on motion, it seems to indicate an intention to publish material already composed or in process of composition.

On the other hand, in a previous memorandum (411.1) he writes: "Alexander thought that he had successfully refuted the opinion of Hipparchus on acceleration at the end of natural motion, when he adduced in opposition the case of natural motion not preceded by forced motion. And, indeed, even Hipparchus did not observe that forced motion preceded every case of natural motion, as we have made clear." Where had he made this clear? Is the reference to ch. 19 of the essay (319–20), or to a previous discussion or lecture on this question?

Some of the memoranda on motion are not utilized in the essay or dialogue on motion, e.g., the analogy of the clock spring (412.15). Others are not directly on the subject of motion, e.g., those that seem to bear on the distinction between mathematics and physics (cf. 410.27, 416.14, 16, 23). There are also references to authors not cited in the essay or the dialogue. The references are not necessarily to the original sources. For example, the reference (411) to Burleus (Walter Burley) and Contarenus (Gaspare Contarini) is a direct quotation from the work of Pereira cited in ch. 19, n. 5.

I conclude with a translation of what I have referred to as a plan or program of a work on motion (418–19). The topics are, for the most part, the same as those of the essay, but there are significant differences of content and order. I note relevant sections of the essay in the case of various items.

418   It may be asked whether heavy bodies really move   toward the center. On this, Ptolemy, *Almagest* 1, ch. 7. [Cf. ch. 2; the question is not actually decided there.]

Will the impressed force be consumed by time or by the weight of the body? [Cf. 335; the question is not fully discussed.]

By what is natural motion caused? [Ch. 1.]

By what is forced motion caused? [Ch. 13; also 361–66.]

Is a medium necessary for motion? [Cf. ch. 10.]

Is there an absolutely heavy and an absolutely light? [Ch. 12.]

Are the elements in their proper place heavy or light? [Ch. 11.]

On the ratio of the [speeds of] motions of the same body in different media. [Ch. 8 (269).]

On the ratio of the [speeds of] motions of different bodies in the same medium. [Ch. 8 (272).]

On the cause of the slowness and speed of motion. [Ch. 7.]

Is there [an interval of] rest at the turning point? [Ch. 20.]

Is natural motion always accelerated and why is it accelerated?
[Ch. 19.]

Is slowness and speed of natural motion due to rareness or
<density of the medium>? [Ch. 7.]

In motion three items are considered: the moving body, the
medium, and the motive force.

Of what help or hindrance is the shape of moving bodies to
their motion? [Cf. 266.]

The ratio of the weights of the same heavy body in different
media, on which depends the question of the ratio [of the speeds]
of their motions. [Ch. 8.]

If the weight of the medium and the speed of the body are
known, the weight of the body is also known. [Cf. ch. 8.]

If the weight of the body and of the medium are known, the
speed of the motion is also known. [Cf. ch. 8.]

If the speed and weight of the body are known, the weight of
the medium is also known. [Cf. ch. 8.]

On circular motion. [Ch. 15, 16.]

To be considered is the ratio [of the speeds] of motions on inclined planes [ch. 14]; and whether it happens that lighter bodies
fall more swiftly at the beginning, just as, in the case of the balance, the smaller the weights, the more easily the motion takes
place. [Ch. 22.]

419   The medium retards natural motion in this way:
for example, when a bell falls, it is, so to speak, a solid
body consisting of air enclosed by the metal, and so it is lighter
than if air were not present.[1]

Lighter bodies move easily so long as they are joined to the
mover; but when they are no longer in contact with the hand
of the mover, <they retain> for only a short time the impetus
<they have received>. [313.11.]

The argument of those who say that [natural] motion is accelerated toward the end for the reason that . . . .

[The rest is mutilated: but the reference seems to be to an argument like that of 317.21, but based on the analogy of drilling a
hole in wood.]

---

1. I.e., if, instead of the bell, there were a solid piece of metal.

ON MECHANICS

Translated with Introduction

and Notes by

Stillman Drake

TO
Herbert M. Evans
Scientist, historian and
bibliophile:
Hence threefold friend
of Galileo, and
triply my instructor.

Introduction

I

Galileo's mature work on mechanics is contained in his *Discourses and Mathematical Demonstrations Concerning Two New Sciences,* which has been translated into English no less than three times and is easily available.[1] The *Two New Sciences,* however, includes almost nothing from the *Mechanics* which Galileo had written some forty years previously for the instruction of his private pupils at the University of Padua. This earlier work, though it was twice rendered into English during the seventeenth century, has ever since remained virtually unobtainable except in Italian.[2] Increasing interest in the development of modern physical science now appears to justify a new translation, especially as the recent appearance in English of a large body of medieval writings on statics and dynamics has left Galileo's *Mechanics* a sort of missing link in our literature of the subject.[3]

The *Mechanics* deals almost exclusively with the analysis of simple machines, a topic omitted from the *Two New Sciences* with the exception of a brief discussion of the lever. The reason for this omission may be found in the fact that the emphasis in the title of Galileo's crowning work was unquestionably on the

1. By Thomas Salusbury in 1662, published in 1665 as the opening part of the second tome of his *Mathematical Collections and Translations;* by Thomas Weston in 1730, because at that time Salusbury's translation was already rare; by Henry Crew and Alfonso de Salvio in 1914, since which time it has been frequently reprinted. References to the *Two New Sciences* herein are to the last-named translation.

2. By Robert Payen in 1636, whose unpublished manuscript translation is now in the British Museum (Harleian MS 6796), and by Thomas Salusbury in the volume cited in the previous note.

3. See especially E. A. Moody and M. Clagett, *The Medieval Science of Weights* (Madison, 1952), and M. Clagett, *The Science of Mechanics in the Middle Ages* (Madison, 1959).

word "new," whereas there was little that he considered novel in
the treatment of simple machines. His preoccupation with confining his published works to new discoveries had already become
evident in a letter written shortly before the invention of the
telescope distracted his attention and energies from the science of
mechanics to other matters for many years. Writing in February,
1609, to Antonio de' Medici, he said:

> Since my return from Florence I have been occupied in some con-
> templations of various experiments pertaining to my treatise on
> mechanics, in which I hope that the greater part will consist of new
> things not touched on by others before. And just recently I have
> completed the discovery of all the conclusions, with proofs, pertaining
> to the strengths and resistances of wooden beams of various lengths,
> sizes, and shapes; how much weaker these are in the middle than at
> the ends, and how much greater weight they can sustain if distributed
> evenly rather than put in one place, and what shape they should
> have in order to be equally strong throughout—a science most neces-
> sary in the construction of machines and of all sorts of buildings, nor
> has anyone treated of this.[4]

A year later, writing to the Tuscan Secretary of State to press
for appointment at that court, Galileo described in the following
words certain books which he wished to complete and publish:

> Three books on local motion, an entirely new science in which
> no one else, ancient or modern, has discovered any of the most re-
> markable laws which I demonstrate to exist in both natural and vio-
> lent movement, whence I may call this a new science and one dis-
> covered by me from its very foundations. Three books on mechanics,
> two relating to its principles and one concerning its problems; and
> though other men have written on this subject, what has been done is
> not one-quarter of what I write, either in quantity or otherwise.[5]

This second group of three books comprised the *Mechanics*
here translated, a book of problems mentioned at the end of it
but now lost, and the book on strength of materials described in
the letter previously cited. Together with an additional work on
the force of cohesion, the last-named eventually became the first
of the "two new sciences" presented to the world in 1638. The
second "new science" included the three books on local motion,
dealing respectively with uniform motion, accelerated motion,
and the motion of projectiles. Although from its finished style it
would appear that Galileo had thought at one time of publishing
the *Mechanics*, the only part of it which he tried to develop in

4. *Opere di Galileo Galilei*, Edizione Nazionale (2d ed.; Florence, 1929–39),
X, 229. This work is hereafter designated by the word *Opere*.

5. *Opere*, X, 351–52.

dialogue form (for inclusion in the *Two New Sciences*) was that which dealt with the force of percussion; the analysis of simple machines seemed to him to present so little novelty as to be unworthy of a place in his final published work, reserved as that was for his original discoveries.

Nevertheless the *Mechanics* in its entirety was so far superior to other available works on the subject at its time that it enjoyed wide circulation in manuscript and was translated into French[6] as well as English during Galileo's lifetime, while the Italian text was published shortly after his death.[7] The precise date at which it was put into its final polished form is difficult if not impossible to determine. Generally it is considered to date from 1600 or earlier; it is most unlikely to have been revised after 1608. In any case it was preceded by a briefer version composed probably in 1593, the first full year of Galileo's residence at Padua, and somewhat revised in the following year.[8] Hence with regard to its essential content, and for all historical purposes, the *Mechanics* may be considered to have followed very shortly after the composition of *De Motu*.

There is evidence that Galileo had no higher opinion of his *Mechanics* than of his elementary treatises on military architecture, fortifications, and cosmography. All these were similarly composed for use either in public or in private instruction at Padua, and Galileo allowed them to circulate in manuscript copies without title or identification of his authorship among those pupils and friends who desired copies. On at least two occasions parts of the *Mechanics* were cited to him as the work of another or an unknown author, without exciting his customary spirited defenses against such attributions of his own work. It is true that much of the content in this case differs little from that of some standard works of the time. Nevertheless, only a pedant or hostile critic of Galileo's would say today that there was nothing essentially new in his *Mechanics*. Even if all the pieces of the puzzle were separately available in the works of Aristotle, Archimedes, Pappus, Philoponus, Jordanus, and others; even if some

6. *Les Mechaniques de Galilée,* tr. Marin Mersenne (Paris, 1634).

7. *Della Scienza Mecanica, e delle Utilità che si traggono di quella,* ed. Luca Danesi (Ravenna, 1649).

8. The early version was published by Favaro in *Memorie del R. Istituto Veneto di scienze, lettere ed arte,* XXVI, 5 (Venice, 1899). Favaro was in some doubt whether the manuscript from which he worked was entirely authentic or was partly a student's notebook. Subsequently this doubt has been removed by the discoveries of similar manuscripts in Hamburg and Pasadena, of which an account has been published in *Osiris,* XIII (1958), 262–90.

had been assembled correctly by Tartaglia, Guido Ubaldi, Benedetti, and Stevin, a coherent and illuminating exposition of the foundations of mechanics can scarcely be said to have preceded it. The principle of virtual velocities in an elementary form affords a good example; if this principle was not new with Galileo, the light which he shed upon its use in this treatise very definitely was. To quote the words of his English biographer of more than a century ago:

The credit of making known the principle of virtual velocities is universally given to Galileo, and so far deservedly, that he undoubtedly perceived the importance of it, and by introducing it everywhere into his writings succeeded in recommending it to others. . . . But although Galileo had the merit in this, as in so many other cases, of familiarizing and reconciling the world to the reception of truth, there are remarkable traces before his time of the employment of this same principle, some of which have been strangely neglected. . . . The principle had been applied directly to determine the proportion [of weights in equilibrium on inclined planes] in a work written long before, where it has remained singularly concealed from the notice of most who have written on this subject. The book bears the name of Jordanus, who lived at Namur[9] in the thirteenth century; but Commandine, who refers to it in his Commentary on Pappus, considers it as the work of an earlier period.[10]

Now the work of Jordanus, whether or not it was overlooked by historians prior to Drinkwater, was so well known in the sixteenth century as to have been considered in the common domain. Tartaglia utilized it freely, intermingled with additions and emendations of his own,[11] and left an edited manuscript of it

---

9. It is not known precisely when or where Jordanus lived. Drinkwater's conjecture that he was of Namur (Belgium) may be rejected. Namur is from Flemish *Namen,* so that the vowel changes required for the traditional Nemorarius associated with the name of Jordanus would be beyond the realm of probability. Pierre Duhem suggested that the place was Nemi, in Italy. More likely Jordanus was of Nemours, in France, the name of which derived originally from Latin *nemora,* a poetic variant of *nemus,* a grove. Such a conjecture fits with the evidence that Jordanus taught in France, at Toulouse. But Jordanus Nemorarius may simply have meant "Jordan the Woodsman," as others have previously suggested.

10. John Elliot Drinkwater(-Bethune), *Life of Galileo, with Illustrations of the Advancement of Experimental Science* (London, 1829), p. 79, col. 1, and p. 82, col. 2. The proof given by Jordanus (or, if Duhem is correct, by an unknown disciple of his) will be found in Moody and Clagett, *The Medieval Science of Weights,* pp. 190–91. While the statement of the theorem is unexceptionable, the demonstration offered is purely geometrical and somewhat lacking in both completeness and rigor, so that the ascription to its author of any particular physical principle will always remain open to objection.

11. *Quesiti et Inventioni Diversi* (Venice, 1546), ff. 81–97.

which was published after his death and about the time Galileo was born.[12] Yet such a distinguished writer on mechanics as Galileo's patron, Guido Ubaldi, failed to draw from it those important insights which are so easily found there by critics who, like Drinkwater, are familiar with the later developments of mechanics. On the contrary, Guido was so scornful of the lack of rigor in the demonstrations of Jordanus as to remain unimpressed by his correct statement of the conditions of equilibrium on inclined planes, adhering rather to an erroneous rule given by Pappus.[13] Nor had Tartaglia been able to progress appreciably beyond Jordanus in mechanics. On the other hand Galileo, who did perceive the importance of the principle of virtual velocities and who proceeded to further correct applications of it, received his clue to the principle not from Jordanus but from Aristotle himself (or rather from the author of the *Mechanical Problems* then ascribed to Aristotle), whom he duly credited.[14] Thus, far from being new, Galileo's most useful tool of analysis was as old as the earliest surviving treatise on mechanics, and yet had remained essentially sterile until he placed it in its proper light.[15] Thereafter this same principle made possible an extraordinarily rapid development of the science of mechanics at the hands of Galileo's pupils and followers, many of them men of less genius than others who had grappled ineffectively with the same problems for centuries.

Rather more of a novelty, and one which has received less attention than it deserves, is the emergence of certain concepts of conservation in the *Mechanics*. The idea of the conservation of energy, so essential in its successive stages to the development of

12. *Jordani Opusculum de Ponderositate, Nicolai Tartaleae studio correctum* (Venice, 1565).

13. *Le Mechaniche dell'Illustriss. Sig. Guido Ubaldo de' Marchesi del Monte,* tr. Filippo Pigafetta (Venice, 1581), f. 121. In another work, *In duos Archimedis aequeponderantium libros paraphrasis* (Pesaro, 1588), pp. 18–19, Guido declared: "And however much Jordanus Nemorarius (whose followers include Nicholas Tartaglia and others) struggled in his book *De ponderibus* [i.e., *De ratione ponderis*] to prove this same proposition of the general lever by many means, yet none of the proofs were worthy of the name 'demonstration,' but were scarcely to be credited. And these, which in no way carry conviction, and perhaps do not even persuade by probability, he put together when in mathematical demonstrations the most precise reasons are required. And on that account it never seemed to me that this Jordanus should even be reckoned among mechanicians."

14. *Opere*, IV, 69.

15. This statement is perhaps unfair to Hero of Alexandria, whose treatise on machines shows clearly that he was in possession of many of the most important concepts linking statics and dynamics some fifteen centuries earlier; this work appears, however, to have remained unknown to European scholars until the latter part of the nineteenth century.

modern physics, had its origins in the recognition that mechanical energy is conserved as such, at least approximately, in some form subject to measurement. It is usual to credit Descartes with the first general notion of conservation in the statement that the total motion in the universe is constant. But prior to this grand generalization there had been some verifiable observations with regard to connected and isolated systems; and it seems to have been Galileo who first perceived clearly that simple machines were incapable of creating force, or work, but merely served to transform its manner of application. It has been said that this was not a true conservation concept because Galileo failed to deny explicitly the possibility of loss or destruction of force or work in machines.[16] Such a denial is, however, implicit in his repeated equation of the product of two quantities (power and space, or force and velocity) at either end of a machine. With this should be contrasted the statements of his contemporaries such as Guido and Stevin, which often seem to assert that, except in states of equilibrium, machines inherently require greater input than they can deliver as output, quite apart from the recognizable effects of friction and other accidental impedances to motion.

Galileo's belief in a conservation principle is still more strikingly illustrated by his attempt to deal with the force of percussion. One may cite also a remark of his which, though not included in the *Mechanics,* is closely akin to it in spirit:

When I say that nature does not permit herself to be overcome nor defrauded by art, I mean (confining myself to the matter in hand) that, there having been conceded to me by nature ten degrees, for example, of force—which is to say the power to equal ten degrees of resistance—she denies to me and prohibits me the overcoming of any resistance that is more than ten degrees; and moreover I add that she prohibits my applying all my force of ten degrees in overcoming or moving a resistance that is of only four or six degrees, or in any way less than ten. For who would say that when with all my force I break a cord, I could employ the same force in breaking a feeble thread? Or that if with all my force I raise a weight of one hundred pounds, I might use the same in raising one of ten? [17]

Again, Galileo's restricted principle of inertia as that begins to appear in *De Motu* is itself a conservation principle that finds some implicit applications in the *Mechanics.* It is very interesting

16. E. Meyerson, *Identity and Reality,* tr. K. Loewenberg (London, 1930), p. 190.
17. *Opere,* VIII, 572–73.

that from the first, Galileo saw some analogy between linear inertial motions and the conservation of angular momentum in
rotating massive bodies. Though it would lead us too far afield to
discuss it here, the basic conservation principle which makes its
appearance in various forms throughout Galileo's works is extremely useful in any attempt to reconstruct the processes by
which an inertial concept first took form in his mind and gradually developed into an implicit assumption.

II

It is often said that Galileo's work represented the revival and
continuation of that of Archimedes, while he had constantly to
combat the influence of Aristotle upon the scholars of his day.
In many areas of dispute this is certainly true, as for example in
hydrostatics, but it is far from being so in the domain covered by
the *Mechanics*. Indeed, almost the reverse holds here; not a
choice, but a reconciliation between the two traditions for dealing
with mechanical problems was required.

Aristotle, who took motion to be the principle of nature, was
much concerned with the relations of movers and things moved.
Hence his approach, and the approach of his followers, was fun-
damentally dynamic; Archimedes, less interested in philosophic
principles than in mathematical proofs, confined his writings to
the investigation of static problems such as the determination of
centers of gravity and conditions of equilibrium. Aristotle wrote:
"If the mover A has moved B a certain distance D in a time T,
then in the same time the same force will move $B/2$ twice the
distance D; for thus the rules of proportion are observed. Again,
if a given force moves a given weight a certain distance in a certain time, and half the distance in half the time, then half the
motive power will move half the weight the same distance in the
same time." So far, so good. But Aristotle continues: "But if E
moves Z a distance D in a time T, it does not necessarily follow
that E can move $2Z$ half the distance in the same time. . . . Otherwise one man might move a ship, since both the motive power
of the shiphaulers and the distance they all cause the ship to
traverse are divisible into as many parts as there are men."[18] This
was sound common sense, and to the followers of Aristotle in the
Middle Ages it remained the *reductio ad absurdum* of any gen-
eralized science of dynamics.

Now Archimedes, whose mechanical skill was in no way in-

18. *Physica*, VII, 5, 249b, 30 ff.

ferior to his mathematical genius, is said to have devised a machine of such power as to enable him actually to move a ship single-handed; but if he ever wrote on the theory of such machines, his analysis has not survived. It was among Galileo's substantial contributions to perceive that just as one can divide the haulers and the distance, so one can divide the ship, enabling any small force to move it, and that the operation of a machine is precisely the equivalent of doing this. The reflection that in effect the small forces would in such a case have to traverse as many times the distance as the single large force would contain of them led Galileo to the notion of equivalence of work at the two ends of a machine. The difficulty of bridging this logical gap, which seems so simple to us, becomes evident when we consider passages from the works of Galileo's older contemporaries such as Guido and Stevin.

Guido's *Mechanics* opened with a long critical discussion of the balance, including mathematical minutiae which Galileo later ignored; but coming next to the lever, in the fourth proposition on that subject he established correctly the equilibrium conditions, and then added this corollary:

From these things it is manifest that the space of [i.e., traversed by] the power that moves has a greater ratio to the space of the weight moved, than the weight to that same power. For the space of the power has the same ratio to the space of the weight as the weight has to the power that sustains the same weight. But the power that sustains is less than the power that moves; therefore the weight has a smaller proportion to the power that moves it than to the power that sustains it. Hence the space of the moving power will have a greater ratio to the space of the weight than the weight has to the same power.[19]

An identical deduction is presented for pulley systems as a corollary to the twenty-sixth proposition concerning pulleys. Thus in Guido's opinion, the supposed difference in ratios is not merely due to friction and other impedances of material systems, but exists as an inherent condition demonstrated by geometry. Nor does Guido attempt to explore the magnitude of the supposed difference, or relate it to speed of motion, or in any other way attempt to deal mathematically with systems in actual motion. It seems rather that for purely logical reasons he despairs of any dynamic analysis.[20]

19. *Le Mechaniche*, f. 39.
20. See note 24 to the *Mechanics*.

A different but equally imaginary logical obstacle to the unifi-
cation of statics and dynamics is seen in the attitude of Stevin,
who rejected the principle of virtual velocities (in its rudimentary
Aristotelian form) on the following grounds:

The cause of equality of apparent weights of unequal gravities
at unequal arms proportional thereto . . . the Ancients . . . considered to reside in the circles described by the extremities of the
arms, as appears in Aristotle's *In Mecanicis* and [among] his successors. This we deny, and we give the following reason therefor:

'That which hangs still, does not describe a circle;
'Two gravities of equal apparent weight hang still;
'Therefore, two gravities of equal apparent weight do not
describe circles.'[21]

These and similar objections to the use of dynamic considerations in static analyses had long prevented the creation of a uni-
fied science of mechanics. Galileo swept them aside when he
wrote in his *Mechanics:* "And since to make the weight *B* descend, any minimal heaviness added to it is sufficient, we shall
leave out of account this insensible quantity and shall not distinguish between the power of one weight to sustain another, and
its power to move it."[22] For by the time he made this remark
Galileo had already realized (as his predecessors had not) that in
theory at least, motion once commenced did not cease without the
interposition of some force. Thus what would have seemed to
his predecessors a brash and arbitrary assumption, against logic
and against common sense, became in the context of Galileo's
work a defensible bridge between statics and dynamics, consistent
with his over-all view of the behavior of heavy bodies. In this and
similar ways the novelty of his *Mechanics,* indiscernible in its
parts, is unmistakable in the whole.

III

The present translation is based upon the text as established by
Antonio Favaro after collation of a dozen manuscript copies and

---

21. *De Beghinselen der Weegconst* (Leyden, 1586), p. 65; English translation
by Miss C. Dikshoorn in *The Principal Works of Simon Stevin,* ed. E. J. Dijks-
terhuis (Amsterdam, 1955), I, 507, 509. That medieval writers felt the same
illogic to exist in such reasoning is evidenced by the remarks of Blasius of Parma,
for which see Moody and Clagett, *The Medieval Science of Weights,* p. 253. In
fairness to Stevin it should be added, however, that his logical scruples did not
prevent his recognition of important practical rules; thus in his book on pulleys
he cited as a "common rule of statics" the evidently dynamic principle of inverse
proportionality of spaces and powers (*Principal Works,* I, 557).
22. *Vide infra,* p. 156.

the earliest printed editions. As an appendix, two chapters have been added concerning compound machines which were included in the versions of 1593–94 but were omitted when Galileo expanded and polished his original lecture syllabus. Departures from Favaro's text have been made only with regard to the division of sentences and paragraphs with a view to ease of reading.

The words *gravità* and *velocità* have been rendered "heaviness" and "speed," in order to avoid the technical connotations of our present-day terms "gravity" and "velocity." The word *forza* presented a problem of translation. Galileo generally favored the word *virtù* for the dynamic concept of force, and used *forza* to mean "power" or "strength." The awkwardness in English of such a phrase as "power of percussion" seemed to forbid the consistent use of "power," and the translation of *forza* sometimes as "force" and sometimes as "power" according to context would require the application of modern standards at the risk of making Galileo appear more advanced in conceptual distinctions than he probably was. Accordingly "force" is used generally for *forza,* and "power" is reserved in this translation for instances in which Galileo used the word *potenza*. Exceptions, as where *forza* is applied in the text to the strength of an animal, are duly noted.

Moment has been italicized throughout, as *momento* is a technical term of Galileo's for which no single modern equivalent exists. Galileo did not adopt the traditional medieval concept of "positional weight," but utilized the word *momento* to combine the notions of weight or force and the effective distance at which this acted. At the same time he recognized that other factors, especially velocity, could enter into the effective action of a weight, and thus he came to apply this word also to the product of weight and velocity. Hence the word *moment* here means sometimes "static moment" and sometimes "momentum."

It may be worth noting that at Galileo's time the word *moment,* which had previously been employed in Latin writings on statics, was new in its technical sense in Italian literature, at any rate in the opinion of certain philosophical critics who undertook to attack Galileo's work on hydrostatics. The first to take up the cudgels complained that the word was "Latin or Ptolemaic, as it is not used in this sense in our modern colloquial language, and still less in our ancient tongue, for in the copious and exquisite Vocabulary of the Crusca I see no example of it."[23] In a marginal

---

23. *Opere*, IV, 158. Ptolemy is said to have written on moments, as was kindly pointed out to Galileo by another of his critics (*ibid.*, p. 385). Guido lamented the loss of Ptolemy's book, which is supposed to have considered upward as well

note Galileo commented: "Your colloquial language fails to use not only this word *moment,* but all the rest of the commonest words in the whole field of mathematics."[24] And in the second edition of his book on floating bodies he inserted the following definition:

Moment, among mechanics, signifies that force, that power, that efficacy, with which the mover moves and the moved body resists, which force depends not only upon simple heaviness, but upon the speed of motion and upon the varying inclinations of the space over which the motion is made, as a descending body has more impetus in a very steep descent than in one less steep. And in sum, whatever the cause of such force, it still retains the name of moment. Nor does it appear to me that this sense should be linguistically novel, for if I am not mistaken we very often say, "This is a weighty matter, but that other is of little moment"; and, "Let us turn to light things, and neglect those of moment"—metaphors that are, I believe, taken from mechanics.[25]

---

as downward moments in the Aristotelian tradition (*Paraphrasis,* p. 16). If, as some authors have suggested, the works of Jordanus were in fact commentaries on a lost work of antiquity, they may afford us a key to the content of Ptolemy's treatise.

24. *Opere,* IV, 158.

25. *Opere,* IV, 68. It is worth noting that in the second edition of the Crusca *Vocabulary* (Venice, 1623) the technical sense of *momento* was duly added.

ON MECHANICS

On the Utilities That Are Derived from the Mechanical Science and from Its Instruments

It has seemed well worthwhile to me, before we descend to the theory of mechanical instruments, to consider in general and to place before our eyes, as it were, just what the advantages are that are drawn from those instruments. This I have judged the more necessary to be done, the more I have seen (unless I am much mistaken) the general run of mechanicians deceived in trying to apply machines to many operations impossible by their nature, with the result that they have remained in error while others have likewise been defrauded of the hope conceived from their promises.[1] These deceptions appear to me to have their principal cause in the belief which these craftsmen have, and continue to hold, in being able to raise very great weights with a small force, as if with their machines they could cheat nature, whose instinct—nay, whose most firm constitution—is that no resistance may be overcome by a force that is not more powerful than it. How false such a belief is, I hope to make most evident with true and rigorous demonstrations that we shall have as we go along.

Meanwhile, since it has been mentioned that the utility which is drawn from machines is not the ability to move with a small force, by means of a machine, those weights which without it could not be moved by the same force, it will not be amiss to

---

1. According to stories narrated by two of Galileo's biographers who had undoubtedly heard them from his own lips, his move from Pisa to Padua was at least partly the result of having offended a "principal personage" of Tuscany (probably Giovanni de' Medici) by giving an unfavorable opinion on some mechanical contrivance devised by that person and approved by others who had been consulted. If such an event took place, the incident was fresh in Galileo's mind when the *Mechanics* was composed during his early years at Padua.

declare what are the advantages brought to us by this study; for if nothing useful were to be expected from it, all the work employed in its acquisition would be vain.

Taking our start, then, from this consideration, there lie before us at first four things to be considered; the first is the weight to be transferred from one place to another; second is the force or power that must move it; third is the distance between the beginning and the end of the motion; and fourth is the time in which the change must be made—which time comes to the same thing as the swiftness and speed of the motion, that motion being determined to be speedier than another which passes an equal distance in less time. Now assigning any determined resistance, and delimiting any force, and noting any distance, there is no doubt whatever that the given weight will be conducted by the given force to the given distance; for even though the force be very small, by dividing the weight into many particles of which each shall not remain superior to the force, and transferring them one at a time, the whole weight will finally be conducted to the appointed place; nor may it reasonably be said at the end of this operation that this great weight has been moved and translated by a force lesser than itself, but rather by a force which has many times repeated that motion and space which will have been traversed only once by the whole weight. From which it appears that the speed of the force has been greater than the resistance of the weight by as many times as this weight is greater than the force, since in the time in which the moving force has repeatedly traversed the interval between the endpoints of the motion, the thing moved has passed over this but a single time; nor may it therefore be said that a greater resistance has been overcome by a smaller force, against the constitution of nature. One could say that the natural arrangement had been overcome only if the lesser force should transfer the greater resistance with its speed of motion equal to that with which the latter travels—which we absolutely affirm to be impossible to accomplish with any machine imagined or imaginable.[2]

But since it may sometimes happen that, having but a small force, we need to move a great weight all at once without dividing it into pieces, on such an occasion it will be necessary to have

---

2. The repudiation of the possibility of perpetual motion which, according to Ernst Mach at least, is a basic principle in the formulation of any sound theoretical mechanics, was to Stevin a static principle. With Galileo it took this dynamic form from which the idea of equivalence readily emerged, as seen in the ensuing sentence.

recourse to the machine, by means of which the given weight will be transferred through the assigned space by the given force; yet this does not remove the necessity for that same force to travel and measure that same (or an equal) space as many times as it is exceeded by the said weight. So that at the end of the action we will find that the only profit we have gained from the machine is to have transported the given weight in one piece with the given force to the given end; which weight, divided into pieces, would have been transported without any machine by the same force in the same time through the same distance. And this must be counted as one of the utilities that are derived by the mechanic; for indeed it often happens that, with a paucity of force but not of time, we must move great weights as units. But whoever hopes and attempts by means of machines to gain the same effect without slowing down the movable body will surely be mistaken, and will demonstrate that he does not understand the nature of mechanical instruments and the reasons for their effects.

Another utility is derived from mechanical instruments, which depends upon the place in which the operation must be carried out, for all the instruments are not adapted to all places with equal convenience. Thus we see (to explain by means of an example) that to draw water from a well we make use of a simple cord, with a container suited to receiving and containing water. With this we procure a determined quantity of water in a certain time with our limited force, and whoever might think himself able by machines of any sort to draw with the same force in the same time a greater quantity of water would be seriously in error; and he would be the more mistaken the more varied and complicated the inventions he might go about contriving.[3] Yet we see water extracted with other instruments, as with pumps to empty the holds of ships. But here it must be noted that pumps were not introduced for this purpose because of their carrying a larger quantity of water in the same time by means of the same force as that required for a simple bucket, but only because in such a place the use of a bucket or similar vessel could not accomplish the desired effect, which is to keep the hold dry of even a small quantity of water; and this the bucket cannot do, not being capable of plunging and submerging where there is no appreciable depth

3. Here Galileo probably referred to the fact, well known to practical artisans, that loss of power attends the multiplication of moving parts. But he may have meant only to stress the increase of self-delusion in seeking very roundabout means to fool and defraud nature, a common characteristic of the inventors of perpetual motion machines.

of water. And thus we see winecellars dried with the same instrument, where the water can be removed only obliquely, which would not be done by the ordinary use of a bucket that is raised and lowered perpendicularly by its rope.

The third and perhaps the greatest advantage brought to us by mechanical instruments is with regard to the mover, either some inanimate force like the flow of a river being utilized, or an animate force of much less expense than would be necessary to maintain human power—as when we make use of the flow of a river to turn mills, or the strength (*forza*) of a horse to effect that for which the power of several men would not suffice. In this way we can gain an advantage also in the raising of water or making other strong exertions which doubtless could be carried out by men in the absence of other devices. For men can take water in a simple container, and raise it, and empty it where it is needed; but since a horse or other such mover lacks reason as well as those instruments which are required in order to grasp the container and empty it at the proper time, returning then to refill it, and is endowed only with strength (*forza*), it is necessary for the mechanic to remedy the natural deficiencies of such a mover by supplying artifices and inventions such that with the mere application of its strength it can carry out the desired effect. And in this there is very great utility, not because those wheels or other machines accomplish the transportation of the same weight with less force or greater speed, or through a larger interval, than could be done without such instruments by an equal but judicious and well-organized force, but rather because the fall of a river costs little or nothing, while the maintenance of a horse or similar animal whose power exceeds that of eight or more men is far less expensive than it would be to sustain and maintain so many men.

These, then, are the utilities that are drawn from mechanical instruments, and not those which, to the deception of so many princes and to their own shame, engineers of little understanding go dreaming about when they apply themselves to impossible undertakings. Of this we shall be assured both by the little that has been hinted thus far, and by much more which will be demonstrated in the course of this treatise, if we but attentively heed what is to be said.

Definitions

That which must be observed in all the demonstrative sciences we must also carry out in this treatise; that is, to propound the definitions of the special terms of this study, and its basic assumptions; from which, as from fertile seeds, will germinate and spring as consequences the causes and true proofs of the properties of all mechanical instruments. Since these concern principally the motions of heavy bodies, let us first determine what heaviness is.

We call *heaviness,* then, that tendency to move naturally downward which, in solid bodies, is found to be caused by the greater or lesser abundance of matter (*materia*) of which they are constituted.[4]

Moment is the tendency to move downward[5] caused not so much by the heaviness of the movable body as by the arrangement which different heavy bodies have among themselves. It is through such *moment* that a less heavy body will often be seen to counterbalance some other of greater heaviness, as in the steelyard a little counterweight is seen to raise a very heavy weight, not by excess of heaviness, but rather by its distance from the suspension of the steelyard. This, combined with the heaviness of the lesser weight, increases its *moment* and impetus to go downward, with which it may exceed the *moment* of the other, heavier weight. Thus *moment* is that impetus to go downward composed of heaviness, position, and of anything else by which this tendency may be caused.[6]

Center of gravity is defined to be that point in every heavy body around which parts of equal *moments* are arranged.[7] Thus, imagining such a body to be suspended and supported from the said point, the parts to the right will balance those to the left, the parts to the fore those to the rear, and those above will balance those below, so that the heavy body thus suspended will not tilt in any direction, but, placed in any location and position, pro-

---

4. The word here defined is *gravità,* and it is interesting that Galileo does not reduce it to weight (*peso*), or state that it is to be measured by weight. The concept of mass as measured separately by quantity of matter is never overtly characterized by Galileo or his contemporaries, though in many instances it seems to be implicit in his ideas. He remarks, for example, that a body in free fall has no weight, and that any force will move a frictionless body on a horizontal plane regardless of its weight.

5. Although Galileo speaks here only of downward motion, he later generalizes the term *moment* to include forces in other directions; see pp. 161 and 177, below.

6. Among the things other than weight and position which Galileo had in mind as a factor in *moment* as he defined it was the velocity of the body; see p. 156, below.

7. This definition is due to Commandino, as Guido had mentioned on the first page of his *Mechanicorum liber;* Guido, however, preferred the definition due to Pappus, which Galileo employs only as an illustration. Guido's objection to the other definition is given at length in his *Paraphrasis,* pp. 9 ff. Archimedes appears to leave the term undefined but more probably the definition was given by him in a work now lost.

vided that it is suspended from the said center, it will remain stable. And this is that point which would go to unite itself with the general center of all heavy things—that is, with the center of the earth—if it could descend in some free medium.

Whence let us draw this supposition: Any heavy body will move downward in such a way that its center of gravity will never depart from the straight line produced from this center (placed at the first point of the motion) to the general center of heavy things. This is a very reasonable assumption; for since this single center must go to join the common center, if not impeded it will necessarily go to meet this by the shortest line, which is the unique straight line.

And in the second place we may suppose: Every heavy body gravitates principally upon its center of gravity and receives therein, as its proper seat, every impetus, every heaviness, and in sum every *moment*.[8]

Finally let us suppose: The center of gravity of two equally heavy bodies is in the middle of that straight line which joins the two said centers; or, truly, two equal bodies suspended at equal distances have the point of equilibrium in the common juncture of these equal distances. Thus, for example, the distance *CE* being equal to the distance *ED*, and from these being suspended two equal weights *A* and *B*, let us suppose the point of equilibrium to be in the point *E*, there being no stronger reason to tilt from one side than from the other.[9]

But here it must be noted that such distances must be measured with perpendicular lines dropped from the point of suspension upon the straight lines drawn from the centers of gravity of the two weights to the common center of heavy bodies.[10] Thus if the

8. That the center of gravity of a body or system of bodies would remain always in the straight line joining its point of departure to the center of the earth, if allowed to fall freely, was a concept that had been used by previous writers; but that the center of gravity might be treated as the seat of every received force or impulse seems to be new with Galileo.

9. This utilization of the principle of sufficient reason is worth noting. The same principle, which underlies Stevin's celebrated demonstration of equilibrium on inclined planes, was also used extensively by Galileo in arriving at and illustrating his limited inertial concept. Here it serves to replace the postulate of Archimedes concerning the inclination of a balance toward the side bearing the heavier weight, which Galileo introduces only implicitly as a further argument.

10. Galileo's unconcern here with regard to the fact that such lines are not parallel is only apparent; the *Mechanics* was intended for elementary instruction, and Galileo did not here involve himself in these points as Guido had done. However, if the following passage is read carefully, it will be seen that the question is skirted, not wrongly treated; this is so characteristic of Galileo that it is not unusual to see contradictions and errors imputed to him which he never made. Concerning his reason for treating the lines directed to the center of the earth as

distance *ED* were carried to *EF*, the weight *B* would not counter-balance the weight *A;* for drawing two straight lines from the centers of gravity to the center of the earth, we see that the line which comes from the center of the weight *J* is closer to the point *E* than this other line produced from the center of the weight *A*. Therefore it must be understood that equal weights are sus-pended from equal distances whenever the straight lines that go from their centers to meet the common center of heavy things shall be equally distant from that straight line which is produced from the boundary of these distances (that is, from the point of suspension) to that same center of the earth.

These things being determined and assumed, let us come to the explanation of a very well known and important principle of the majority of mechanical instruments, demonstrating how unequal weights hanging from unequal distances will weigh equally whenever the said distances are inversely proportional to the weights. That unequal weights weigh equally when suspended from unequal distances which are inversely proportional to these weights, we shall not only demonstrate to be true in the way in which we are certain of the truth of the principle stated above, where it is assumed that equal weights weigh equally from equal distances, but we shall demonstrate this to be precisely the same thing, and that there is no difference between suspending un-equal weights from inversely proportional distances, and equal weights from equal distances.

Therefore imagine the heavy solid *CFDE*, of uniform density and of uniform size throughout, such as a cylinder or similar

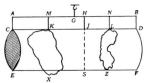

figure. Let this be suspended by its endpoints *C* and *D*, from the line *AB*, equal in length to the solid. Now dividing this line *AB* equally at the point *G*, and suspending it from this point, there can be no doubt that it will balance in this point *G*, because the line drawn from this point straight to the center of the earth would pass through the center of gravity of the solid *CF*. And of the latter, parts of equal *moments* would exist around such a line;

---

parallel in practical problems, see *Opere*, VIII, 274–75 (*Two New Sciences*, pp. 250–51). The curious antipathy of Duhem toward Galileo is strikingly illus-trated by his characterization of the same reasons when given by Torricelli as "profoundly different from those of Galileo" (*Les Origines* . . ., II, 153–54).

and it would be the same if from the points A and B there were
suspended the two halves of the heavy body CF. Next suppose
the said heavy body to be cut into two unequal parts along the
line $JS;$ it is obvious that the part CS (as also the other part SD)
would no longer remain in position, having no other supports
than the two strings AC and BD. Therefore, coming to the point
J, suppose a new string to be added, tied at the point H perpendicularly above the cut $JS;$ this then sustains jointly both parts of
the solid in their pristine state. Hence it follows that no change
being made either of weight or of position in the parts of the solid
with respect to the line AB, the same point G remains the center
of equilibrium as it has been from the first. Moreover, since the
part CS of the solid is connected to the balance through the two
strings CA and JH, there can be no doubt that if we cut these
two strings and add a single other at MK, equidistant from these
two, then since the center of gravity of the solid CS lies directly
beneath this, the solid will not change or move its place, but will
keep the same position with respect to the line AH. And doing
the same with the other part, JF (that is, cutting the strings HJ
and BD, and adding in the center the sole suspension NL), it is
likewise apparent that this will not vary its site or relation with
respect to the balance AB. Hence the parts of the whole solid CF
being the same with respect to the balance AB as they have been
all along, CS hanging from the point M and SD from the point
N, there is no doubt that equilibrium will still exist at the same
point G. Now here it begins to become apparent that the two
weights CS (the greater) and SD (the lesser), hanging from the
ends of the line MN, must be of equal *moment* and give rise to
equilibrium in the point G, the distance GN being greater than
GM.[11]

To carry out our full intent it now remains only for us to demonstrate that the ratio which exists between the weights CS and
SD exists also between the distances NG and $GM;$ and this will
not be difficult to prove. For the line MH being one-half the line
HA, and NH being half of HB, all MN will be one-half the
whole line AB, of which BG is also one-half. Hence MN and
GB will be equal to one another; and from these taking away

11. The ingenuity (and fallacy) of Galileo's demonstration has been sufficiently recognized elsewhere; see, for instance, Ernst Mach, *Science of Mechanics*
(Lasalle, 1942), pp. 17 ff. Here it is important to note that though he departs
from Archimedes, he does not adopt the Aristotelian demonstration depending
upon virtual velocities (*Mechanical Problems*, Int. and Sec. 3), which he brings
in only later as a "probable" (in contrast with rigorous) support in the "Observations" which follow his own demonstration.

the common part *GN*, the remainder *MG* will be equal to the remainder *NB*, to which *NH* is likewise equal; whence *MG* is equal to *NH;* and adding the part *GH* to both, *MH* will equal *GN*. Now, having already demonstrated that *MG* equals *HN*, that proportion which the line *MH* has to *HN*, the distance *NG* will have to the distance *GM;* but the proportion *MH* to *HN* is that of *KJ* to *JL*, and of its double *CJ* to the double *JD*—and in a word, of the solid *CS* to the solid *SD*, of which solids the lines *CI* and *ID* are the lengths. Hence it is concluded that the ratio of the distance *NG* to the distance *GM* is the same as that of the size of the solid *CS* to the size of the solid *SD;* which, manifestly, is the same as the ratio of the weights (*gravità*) of those same solids.

And from what has been said it seems to me clearly understood not only how the two unequal heavy bodies *CS* and *SD* weigh equally when hanging from distances inversely proportional [to their weights], but moreover how, in the nature of things, this is the same effect as if equal weights were suspended at equal distances, since in a certain sense the heaviness of the weight *CS* virtually spreads out beyond the support at *G*, and that of the weight *SD* shrinks back from it, as any speculative mind can understand by examining closely what has been said about the present diagram. And, the same heaviness of the weights and the same boundaries of the suspensions being maintained, even though the shapes are varied by reduction to spherical or other forms such as *X* and *Z*, it will not be doubted that the same equilibrium will follow, shape being a qualitative circumstance (*accidente di qualità*) and powerless to alter the weight, which derives rather from the quantity. Whence we conclude generally that it is true that unequal weights weigh equally when suspended inversely from unequal distances having the same ratio as the weights.

Some Observations About the Things Said Above

Having shown how the *moments* of unequal weights are equalized by being suspended inversely at distances having the same ratio, it seems to me that we should not pass by in silence another agreement and probability by which the same truth may reasonably be confirmed to us.

Therefore consider the balance *AB* divided into unequal parts at the point *C*, and weights having the proportion of the distances *BC* and *CA* suspended respectively from the points *A* and *B*. It is already manifest how the one will counterbalance the other, and consequently how if to one of these there was given the least

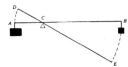

moment of heaviness, it would move downward, raising the other. Thus upon the addition of an insensible weight to the heavy body *B,* the balance would move, the point *B* descending toward *E,* and the other end *A* rising to *D.* And since to make the weight *B* descend, any minimal heaviness added to it is sufficient, we shall leave out of account this insensible quantity and shall not distinguish between the power of one weight to sustain another, and its power to move it.

Now considering the motion made by the heavy body *B* descending to *E,* and that made by the other body *A* ascending to *D,* we shall find without any doubt that the space *BE* is as many times greater than the space *AD* as the distance *BC* is greater than *CA.*[12] For at the center *C* two angles *DCA* and *ECB* are formed which are equal by being opposite, and consequently the two arcs *BE* and *AD* are similar and bear the same proportion as the radii *BC* and *CA* by which they are described. Thus the speed of motion of the heavy body *B* in descending comes to be as much greater than the speed of the other body *A* in rising, as the heaviness of the latter exceeds that of the former.[13] Nor is it any wonder that the weight *A* cannot be raised to *D,* though slowly, unless the other heavy body *B* is moved to *E* swiftly; and it is not foreign to the arrangement of nature that the speed of the motion of the heavy body *B* should compensate the greater resistance of the weight *A* when this moves more weakly to *D* and the other descends more rapidly to *E.* And thus, conversely, the heavy body *A* being placed at the point *D* and the other at the point *E,* it will not be unreasonable that the former, falling slowly to *A,* raises the latter swiftly to *B,* restoring with its heaviness that which comes to be lost by its slowness of motion. And from this reasoning we may arrive at the knowledge that the speed of motion is capable of increasing *moment* in the movable body in the same proportion as that in which this speed of motion is increased.[14]

There is one other thing that must be considered before pro-

12. Here is introduced the double aspect of virtual displacements and of virtual velocities, the latter especially being an ancient Aristotelian heritage which Duhem considered to be the exclusive basis of Galileo's dynamics (*Les Origines,* i, 255).

13. The introduction of speed (*velocità*) as directly proportional to displacement is of great consequence to the development of Galileo's generalization of moment from its traditional static to a new dynamic concept (momentum); see also *Opere,* VII, 241–42 (*Dialogue,* pp. 213–15).

14. The concept of momentum in general follows directly from this, but Galileo never completely dissociated his analysis of *moment* from connected systems. See, however, his discussions below of the inclined plane and of the force of percussion.

ceeding further, and this concerns the distances at which heavy bodies come to be weighed; for it is very important to know the sense in which equal and unequal distances are to be understood, and in what manner they must be measured. For given the straight line *AB* and two equal weights hanging from its extremities, and the point *C* being taken in the middle of this line, then equilibrium will exist at this point, and this is so because the distance *AC* equals the distance *CB*. But if the line *CB* is elevated and turned about the point *C*, it will be transferred to *CD*, so that the balance stands according to the lines *AC* and *CD*, and then the two equal weights hanging from the ends *A* and *D* will no longer weigh equally upon the point *C*, because the distance of the weight placed at *D* is made less than it was when located at *B*.

So if we consider the lines along which the said heavy bodies make their impetus and would descend if they moved freely, there is no doubt whatever that these would be the lines *AG*, *DF*, and *BH*. Thus the weight hanging from the point *D* makes its

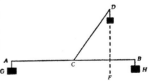

moment and impetus along the line *DF*, but when it hangs from the point *B* its impetus is made along the line *BH;* and since this line *DF* remains closer to the support *C* than does the line *BH*, we must understand the weights to be at equal distances from the point *C*, not when hanging from the points *A* and *D*, but rather when they are ranged along the straight line *ACB*. And finally one must take care to measure the distances with lines which fall at right angles upon those in which the heavy bodies are hanging, and along which they would move if they descended freely.

Of the Steelyard and of the Lever

Now that we have understood through a sure proof one of the prime principles from which, as from a most fertile source, many of the mechanical instruments derive, we will be able to acquire a knowledge of the nature of these without any difficulty whatever.

And first, speaking of the steelyard,[15] a very widely used instrument with which various kinds of merchandise are weighed, even though extremely heavy, by the weight of a small counter-

---

15. *Stadera*, also called the Roman balance; Galileo's terms for its parts are used untranslated below. Guido's translator called the counterpoise *marco* and the arm of the balance *fusto*.

poise (commonly called the *romano*), we shall prove that in such operations nothing more is done than to reduce to a practical act precisely that on which we have theorized above. For let us suppose *AB* to be a steelyard whose support (called *trutina*) is at the point *C*, near which at a small distance *CA* hangs the heavy weight *D;* and along the greater distance *CB* (called the *ago* of the steelyard) there runs back and forth the *romano E*, of small weight in comparison with the heavy body *D*, yet nevertheless capable of moving far enough from the *trutina C* so that the proportion existing between the two weights *D* and *E* may exist between the distances *FC* and *CA;* and then equilibrium will be made, unequal weights being found hanging at distances inversely proportional to them.

Nor is this instrument different from that other called the *vette*, or commonly the lever, with which very large stones and other weights are moved with a small force. Its application is according to the next diagram where the lever is denoted by the bar *BCD*, of wood or other solid material; the heavy weight to be raised is *A*, and a firm support or fulcrum upon which the lever presses and moves is designated *E*. Placing one end of the lever under the weight *A*, as is seen at the point *B*, the force weighing down at the other end *D*, though small, will be able to raise the weight *A*, so long as the proportion of the distance *BC* to *CD* exists between the force placed at *D* and the resistance made by

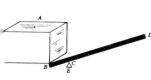

the heavy body *A* upon the point *B*. From which it is made clear that the more closely the support *E* approaches the extremity *B*, increasing the proportion of the distance *DC* to the distance *CB*, the more the force at *D* may be diminished in raising the weight *A*.

Here it should be noted (as also in its place the same will be noted about all the other mechanical instruments) that the utility which is drawn from this instrument is not that of which common mechanics persuade themselves; that is, that nature comes to be overpowered and in a sense cheated, some very great resistance being conquered with a small force by the intervention of the lever. For let us demonstrate that without the aid of the length of the lever the same effect may be accomplished with the same force within the same time. Taking again the same lever *BCD*, of which *C* is the support, and making the distance *CD* five times the distance *CB*, for example, let the lever move until it takes the position *JCG*, when the force will have passed through the space *DJ*, and the weight will have been moved from *B* to *G;* and since

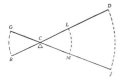

the distance *DC* has been assumed to be five times *CB*, it is obvious from what has been demonstrated that the weight placed at *B* can be five times the moving force placed at *D*. But if, on the other hand, we keep in mind the travel made by the force from *D* to *J* while the weight is moved from *B* to *G*, we shall recognize likewise that the journey *DJ* is five times that of the space *BG*. Moreover, if we take the distance *CL* equal to the distance *CB* and assume the same force at the point *L* that was at the point *D*, and place at the point *B* only the fifth part of the weight that was moved before, there is no doubt that the force at *L* having become equal to this weight at *B*, and the spaces *LC* and *CB* being equal, the said force moved through the space *LM* will transfer a weight equal to itself through the other equal interval *BG;* and that repeating this same action five times, it will transfer all the parts of the said weight to the same point *G*. But to repeat the space *ML* is certainly nothing more nor less than to traverse a single time the interval *DJ*, five times this *LM*.[16] Therefore to transfer the weight from *B* to *G* requires no less force and no less time or any shorter travel at *D*, than what is required when applied at *L*. And to sum up, the advantage acquired from the length of the lever *CD* is nothing but the ability to move all at once that heavy body which could be conducted only in pieces by the same force, during the same time, and with an equal motion, without the benefit of the lever.

Of the Windlass, and of the Capstan

The two instruments whose nature we are now about to explain depend directly upon the lever, and indeed are nothing but a perpetual lever. For if we think of the lever *BAC* supported at the point *A*, and the weight *G* hanging from the point *B*, the force being placed at *C*, it is evident that by transferring the lever to the position *DAE*, the weight *G* will rise through the distance *BD*, but that it cannot continue to be elevated much more. Accordingly if it is still desired to raise it further, it will be necessary to fix it in this position with some other support, and return the lever to its previous place *BAC;* then, taking hold of the weight again, to raise it once more through a similar height *BD*. In this way, doing the same thing many times, the raising of the weight

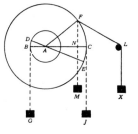

16. Guido, who devoted some fifty-five folios of his *Mechanics* to the analysis of the balance and the lever, and in doing so attacked many problems of interest not dealt with by previous authors, did not arrive at this general idea, which leads to the first conception of conservation of work. The reader will see presently how Galileo applies analogous ideas to each simple machine in turn, and then assumes its general truth in attempting to analyze the force of percussion.

may be accomplished with an interrupted motion, which in many respects may turn out to be not very convenient. Hence this difficulty has been overcome by finding a way of uniting together as it were infinite levers, perpetuating the operation without any interruption whatever. This is done by making a wheel of radius *AC* about the center *A*, with an axle of radius *AB*, all of stout wood or some other firm and solid material, and then sustaining the entire framework on a pivot at the center *A* which passes from one side to the other and is mounted on two strong supports. The cord *DBG*, from which hangs the weight *G*, passes round the axle, and another cord is applied round the larger circle, from which is hung the weight *J*. And the length *CA* being to *AB* in the same ratio as the weight *G* to the weight *J*, the latter will be able to sustain the weight *G*, and with any little additional *moment* will move it.[17]

Now since the axle always turns with the wheel, the cords which sustain the weights always hang tangent to the circumferences of the wheel and axle, maintaining a similar position and relation to the distances *BA* and *AC*. Thus the motion will come to be perpetuated, the weight *J* descending and constraining *G* to rise. But the necessity must be noted of having the cord go round the wheel so that the weight *J* hangs along the tangent line to the rim of the wheel, for if the same weight were suspended so as to hang from the point *F*, cutting the wheel (as may be seen) by the line *FNM*, the motion would no longer be made, the *moment* of the weight *M* being diminished so that it would bear down no more than if it hung from the point *N*. For its distance of suspension from the point *A* is now determined by the line *AN*, perpendicular to the cord *FM*, and not by the radius *AF* of the wheel, which falls at changing (*diseguali*) angles upon the said line *FM*.

Thus when the force is exerted on the wheel by a heavy and inanimate body which has no other impetus than to go downward, it is necessary for this to be suspended by the line tangent to the wheel and not cutting it. But if on the same circumference the force were to be exerted by an animate force which had *moment* to make impetus in all directions, then the effect might

17. It is worth noting that this is rather more than a repetition of the dynamic-static relation mentioned in the introduction and given at p. 156, for meanwhile Galileo has added the concept of increase of *moment* in proportion to velocity (n. 14), and he is now dealing with a machine in which the object to be moved is not necessarily a free weight, but may be something hauled or dragged, as suggested in the next paragraph. Hence this is another slight step toward the dissociation of the concept of force from that of the action of weight.

be made at any point on the circumference; thus, placed at *F* it would lift the weight *G* by rotating the wheel, pulling not downward along the line *FM,* but transversely along the tangent *FL,* which will make a right angle with the line drawn from the center *A* to the point of contact. For the distance from the center *A* to the force placed at *F* being in this way measured by the line *AF* perpendicular to *FL,* along which the impetus is given, the form of the use of the lever has been altered in no way. And note that the same might also be done with an inanimate force, provided that a way were found to arrange to have its *moment* give an impetus pulling at the point *F* along the tangent line *FL,* which could be done by adding a pulley under the line *FL* and passing over this the cord wound round the wheel.[18] This is seen in the line *FLX,* with the weight *X* hanging from its extremity, equal to the weight *J.* This, exercising its force along the line *FL,* will maintain a distance from the center *A* always equal to the radius of the wheel. And from what has been explained, we may draw the conclusion that in this instrument the proportion of the force to the weight will always be the same as the radius of the axle to the radius of the wheel.

From the instrument just explained, that which is called the capstan does not much differ as to form; indeed, it does not differ at all except in mode of application, the windlass being arranged and moved vertically, and the capstan being worked horizontally. If we imagine to be placed upon the circle *DAE* a columnar axle which rotates about the center *B,* and the cord *DH* wound round it and attached to the weight to be drawn, and if into the axle is inserted the bar *FEBD,* at whose extremity *F* is applied the force of a man, or a horse or some other draught animal, which moving around travels about the circumference of the circle *FGC,* then we shall have conceived the capstan. Carrying the bar *FBD* around will turn the axle or drum of the capstan *EAD,* and the heavy body *H* will be constrained to advance by the cord wound round this. And since the point of support round which the motion is made is the center *B,* while the mover is distant therefrom by the line *BF,* and the resisting body by the interval *BD,* the lever *FBD* comes to be formed, in virtue of which the force acquires *moment* equal to the resistance whenever it has to this the

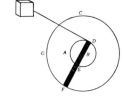

---

18. In these generalizations of directions of forces and in the replacement of any force by a freely hanging weight, Galileo had been anticipated several years previously by Stevin; see especially *Principal Works,* I, 349–53. The technique was of the utmost importance to later theorists; cf. Mach, *Science of Mechanics,* pp. 72–82 in the translation previously cited.

proportion that exists between the lines *DB* and *BF;* that is, the radius of the axle to the radius of the circle on whose circumference the force moves.

In both these instruments, that is to be noted which has often been remarked already: the utility adduced by these machines is not that with which the common people are deceived into believing by the mechanics, which is that nature is defrauded by their machines and that they can overcome her resistance, though great, by means of a small force. For we shall make it manifest how the same force placed at *F* will in the same time, making the same motion, conduct the same weight to the same distance without any machine whatever. Assume, for example, that the weight *H* is ten times the force placed at *F;* in order to move the said resistance it will be necessary that the line *FB* shall be ten times *BD,* and consequently that the circumference of the circle *FGC* shall also be ten times the circumference *EAD.* And since when the force is moved once round the entire circumference of the circle *FGC,* the axle *EAD* (round which is wrapped the cord drawing the weight) will likewise have gone round once, it is obvious that the weight *H* will be moved only the tenth part of the distance traveled by the mover. Hence if the force moving a greater resistance than itself through a given space by means of this machine must be moved ten times as much, there is no doubt that by dividing the weight in ten parts, each of these will be equal to the force; and consequently you would have been able to transport them one at a time over the interval through which you yourself will move; so that by making ten trips, each equal to the circumference *AED,* you would not have traveled farther than once round the circumference *FGC,* and you would have conducted the same weight *H* through the same distance. Therefore the advantage that is drawn from these machines is that of conducting the whole weight at once, but with no less work,[19] and no more speed, nor through any greater distance than that of the same force conducting it part by part.

Of Pulleys[20]

The instruments whose nature may be reduced to the balance as their principle and basis are those already explained, and others

19. It is interesting here that Galileo uses the colloquial expression for work (*fatica*); though he was thinking of "felt effort" and not of the product of force and space traversed.

20. *Taglie;* that is, combination of pulleys in housing, as in our block-and-tackle. The words *girelle* (simple pulleys) and *taglie* have been both rendered here by the same English word for want of suitable distinction.

which differ very little therefrom. Now in order to understand what is to be said of the nature of pulleys, we must first theorize about another method of using the lever, which will yield us much concerning the investigation of the force of pulleys and the understanding of other mechanical effects.

The use of the lever explained above placed the weight at one of its extremities and the force at the other, while the support was placed somewhere between the extremities. But we can use the lever in another way too, placing the support at the extremity *A* (as seen in the diagram), the force at the other extremity *C*, and hanging the weight *D* from some point between, as at the point *B*. This way it is clear that if the weight hung from a point equidistant from the two extremities *A* and *C*, as at the point *F*, the work of supporting it would be equally divided between the two points *A* and *C*, so that half the weight would be felt by the force *C*, the other half being sustained by the support *A*. But if the weight is hung at any other point, as from *B*, we shall show the force at *C* to be sufficient to sustain the weight at *B* so long as it has to that the proportion which the distance *AB* has to the distance *AC*.

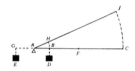

For proof of this, let us imagine *BA* to be prolonged in a straight line to *G*, and let the distance *BA* equal *AG*, and make the weight *E* hanging from *G* equal to the weight at *D*. It is obvious that by the equality of the weights *E* and *D* and the distances *GA* and *AB*, the *moment* of the weight *E* will equal the *moment* of the weight *D*, and will be sufficient to sustain it. Therefore any force that will have a *moment* equal to that of the weight *E*, and will be able to sustain it, will also suffice to support the weight *D*. But if to sustain the weight *E*, we place at the point *C* a force whose *moment* has that proportion to the *moment* of the weight *E* which the distance *GA* has to the distance *AC*, this will be sufficient to support it; hence the same force will be capable of sustaining also the weight *D*, whose *moment* is equal to that of the weight *E*. But the proportion of the lines *GA* and *AC* exists also between *AB* and *AC*, *GA* being equal to *AB*; and since the weights *E* and *D* are equal, each of them will have that same proportion to the force placed at *C*; whence it is concluded that the force at *C* will equal the moment of the weight *D* whenever it has to it that proportion which the distance *BA* has to the distance *CA*. And in moving the weight with the lever used in this mode also it is to be understood, as in the other instruments, that whatever is gained in force is lost in speed.[21] For the force *C*

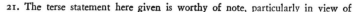

21. The terse statement here given is worthy of note, particularly in view of

elevating the lever and transferring it to *AJ*, the weight is moved through the interval *BH*, which is as much less than the space *CJ* traversed by the force as the distance *AB* is less than the distance *AC*; that is, as much as the force is less than the weight.

These principles explained, let us pass to the theory of pulleys, whose construction and arrangement will be explained together with their uses. And first think of the pulley *ABC* made of metal or hard wood, turning about its axle that passes through the center *D*; and round this pulley place the cord *EABCF*, from one end of which hangs the weight *E*, and at the other assume the force *F*. I say that the weight will be sustained by a force equal to itself, nor will the upper pulley *ABC* give any benefit with regard to moving or sustaining the said weight with the force placed at *F*. For if from the center *D*, which serves as support, we suppose two lines to be drawn to the circumference of the pulley at the point *A* and *C* at which the cords touch the circumference, we shall have a balance of equal arms, the equal radii *DA* and *DC* determining the distances of the two suspensions from the support and center *D*. Whence it is obvious that the weight hanging from *A* cannot be sustained by a lesser weight hanging from *C*, but they must be equal, for such is the nature of equal weights hanging at equal distances. And although the force *F* in moving downward turns the pulley *ABC*, the position and relation between the force and the weight is not changed with respect to the two distances *AD* and *DC*; indeed, the pulley rotated becomes a balance similar to *AC*, but perpetual. From this we can see how childishly Aristotle deceived himself when he supposed that by enlarging the pulley *ABC* one could lift the weight with less work, considering that with the growth of the pulley the distance *DC* was increased, but failing to consider that the distance of the weight is equally increased; that is, the other radius *DA*.[22] The advantage that can be drawn from such an instrument has therefore nothing to do with the diminution of work. And if anyone should ask why it is that on many occasions in raising weights this kind of device is used, as is seen for example in drawing water from a well, one may reply that it is done because in this way the mode of exercising and applying the force turns out to be more convenient. For when we draw anything downward, the weight of our own arms and other members aids us, whereas

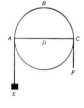

the fact that Galileo's word *forza* might even better be rendered as "power" than as "force" (see Introduction, p. 144).

22. *Mechanical Problems*, sec. 9.

when we must draw the same weight upwards by means only of the vigor of our members and muscles, or, to use the common expression, "by elbow grease," we must raise in addition to the external weight the weight of our own arms, which requires more work. So we conclude that this upper pulley brings us no ease with respect to the force considered simply, but only in the mode of applying it.

But if we make use of a similar machine in another manner, as we are now about to explain, we can lift the weight with less force. For let there be a pulley *BDC* turning about the center *E*, arranged in its box or housing *BLC*, from which is suspended the heavy body *G;* and pass about the pulley the cord *ABDCF* whose end *A* is fixed to some stable fastening. Let the force be placed at the other end *F*, which, moving toward *H*, will raise the framework *BLC* and accordingly the weight *G;* and in this operation I say that the force at *F* will be one-half the weight sustained by it. For the said weight coming straight from the two cords *AB* and *FC*, it is an evident thing that the work is equally divided between the force *F* and the support *A*. And examining more closely the nature of this instrument, let us extend the diameter of the pulley *BEC* and we shall see that a lever is made from whose center (that is, under the point *E*) hangs the heavy body; and the support comes to be at the extremity *B*, while the force is at the extremity *C*. Then by what was explained above, the force will have to the weight the same proportion that the distance *EB* has to the distance *BC* and will therefore be one-half the weight. And although in raising the force toward *H* the pulley turns, there is no change in the relation and arrangement existing between the weight *B*, the center *E* from which the weight hangs, and the extremity *C* at which the force acts. In the turning, the points *B* and *C* change in name but not in nature, others succeeding continually in their places; and thus the lever *BC* perpetuates itself. Here, as in the other instruments and in those to follow, let us not fail to consider how the travel of the force comes to be double that of the weight. For when the weight is moved until the line *BC* has come to have its points *B* and *C* at the points *A* and *F*, the two equal cords *AB* and *FC* will necessarily be extended in a single line *FH;* and consequently when the weight is raised through the interval *BA*, the force will have moved double this, that is from *F* to *H*.

Next, consider that the force placed at *F* must move upward in order to raise the weight, which is impossible for inanimate movers, which for the most part are heavy bodies, and if not im-

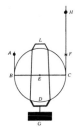

possible at least more laborious for animate ones than exerting
force downward. To overcome this inconvenience, a remedy has
been found by adding another pulley above, as seen in the next
diagram.

Here the cord *CEFG* is made to pass round the upper pulley
FG supported by the hook *L*, so that the cord being passed to *H*
and the force *E* being transferred thence, it will be able to move
the weight *X* by pulling down. But it will not be less thereby
than it was at *E*, since the *moments* of the forces *E* and *H*, hanging from the equal distances *FD* and *DG* of the upper pulley,
remain always equal; nor does this upper pulley, as already
shown, provide any diminution in the work. And it having been
necessary already, through the addition of the upper pulley, to
introduce the hook *L* by which it is sustained, it will be of some
convenience to omit the other, *A*, to which one end of the cord
was attached, and transfer the latter to a ring or to another hook
on the lower part of the box or housing of the upper pulley, as
you see done at *M*. Now finally all this framework composed of
upper and lower pulleys is that which the Greeks call *trochlea*,
and we in Tuscan fashion call *taglie*.[23]

Up to this point we have explained how the force can be
doubled by means of pulleys. It remains for us to demonstrate, as
briefly as possible, the method of increasing it to any degree; let
us first speak of multiplication by even numbers, and later by odd
numbers. In order to show how the force may be multiplied four
times, we shall propose the following theorem as a lemma for the
things that ensue.[24]

---

23. Galileo's word is *toscanamente*, perhaps because when teaching at Padua
he liked to emphasize his Tuscan origin, or perhaps because he fancied that there
was some etymological connection between *trochlea* and *taglie*. Similarly one
might suppose a connection to exist between the latter word and the English
tackle, but such is not the case.

24. The ensuing mode of analysis is set forth by Guido in *Le Mechaniche*, ff.
64v.–68r. He applies it to a large number of pulley combinations successfully, and
presently comes to this promising corollary: "The weight is to the power that
sustains it, as the space of the power is to the space of the weight" (*ibid.*, f. 79r.).
But the implications are not developed by Guido, for we find the same proposition
concerning the windlass at f. 105r., followed immediately by this corollary: "The
space of the moving power is always in greater proportion to the space of the
weight moved, than the weight to the same power." That is, Guido continues
to distinguish between a sustaining power and a moving power, and, for lack of
the simple bridge between statics and dynamics, is unable to formulate quantitative laws for the latter. Thus in speaking of the lever (*ibid.*, ff. 39r.–v.) he had
reasoned: "The space of the power that moves is always in greater proportion to
the space of the weight moved than the weight to the same power. For the space
of the power to the space of the weight is the same as that of the weight to the
power that sustains the weight. But the power that sustains is less than the power

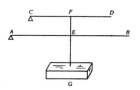

Let there be the two levers *AB* and *CD*, with their supports at the extremities *A* and *C*, and from the centers *E* and *F* of both these let there hang the heavy body *G* supported by two forces of equal *moment* placed at *B* and *D*. I say that the *moment* of each of these equals the *moment* of the fourth part of the weight *G*. For if the two forces *B* and *D* sustained equally, it is clear that the force *D* would be opposed by only one-half the weight *G;* but when the force *D* supports, with the aid of the lever *DC*, one-half of the weight *G* hanging from *F*, it has already been demonstrated that this force *D* has to the weight thus sustained by it that proportion which the distance *FC* has to the distance *CD*, which is the ratio of one to two; therefore the *moment D* is one-half the *moment* of half the weight *G* sustained by it, and consequently it is one-fourth the *moment* of the whole weight. In the same way the same will be proved of the *moment B*. And the weight *G* being supported by the four points *A*, *B*, *C*, and *D* equally, it is quite reasonable that each of these should bear one-fourth of the work.

Next, we come to apply this consideration to the pulleys. Suppose the weight *X* hanging from the two lower pulleys *AB* and *DE*, the cord being wound round these and the upper pulley *GH* as seen by the line *JDEHGAB*, the whole frame being sustained by the point *K*. I say next that the force applied at *M* will be able to sustain the weight *X* when it is equal to one-quarter of this. For if we imagine the two diameters *DE* and *AB*, and the weight hanging from the midpoints *F* and *C*, we shall have two levers similar to those already explained, the fulcrums of which correspond to the points *D* and *A;* whence the force placed at *B*, or let

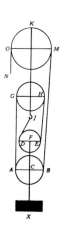

---

that moves; therefore the weight will have a lesser proportion to the power that moves than to the power that sustains. Hence," etc. The logic appears impeccable; yet the contradiction, especially in the case of such a simply connected system as the lever, is so glaring as to be almost incredible. Guido does not perceive that he has passed from "sustains" to "moves" on the part of the power, but not from "is sustained" to "is moved" on the part of the weight. He does not reduce the additional weight or power to an insensible quantity as a tool of analysis, as Galileo does; hence he has to believe that some power (or worse yet, some space) is lost.

Experience bore Guido out in a sense, as some power *is* lost in actual simple machines; space also seems to be lost because ropes stretch, and levers bend, or compress, or are compressed, or slip before taking hold. Yet Guido was in the habit of showing side by side material machines and schematic figures of them, and as a mathematician he should have been able to see the idealized truth. The fact that he did not is strong evidence that it is simpler for us to see this than it was for Galileo, who was the first to do so. Nor is this surprising; it was he who made it simpler for us. In fact, he made it so simple that his critics now are unable to believe that it escaped his predecessors.

us say at M, will be able to sustain the weight X if it is the fourth part of this. And if we then add another upper pulley, making the cord pass to MON, transferring the force M to N, it will be able to sustain the same weight pulling downward, the uppermost pulley neither increasing nor diminishing the force, as explained before. And let us note likewise that in order to raise the weight, the four cords BM, EH, DJ, and AG must travel, so that the mover must journey as much as the length of these four cords; and yet, the weight will not move more than the length of one of these. This is said as a notice and confirmation of that which has been said so often; that is, that in proportion as the work of the mover is lessened, the length of his journey is increased.

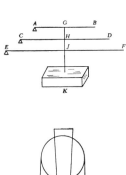

But if we want to increase the force in a sextuple ratio, we shall have to add another pulley to the lower block, which will be better understood if we have before us the present theory. Suppose then the three levers AB, CD, and EF, and from their midpoints G, H, and J the weight K hanging jointly; and at the extremities B, D, and F three equal powers that sustain this weight K, so that each lever carries one-third of this. Since the power at B, sustaining the hanging weight at G by means of the lever BA, amounts to one-half of this weight, which has already been said to be one-third of the weight K, the *moment* of the force B is equal to one-half of the third part of the weight K; that is, one-sixth of it. And the same is shown of the other forces D and F, from which we can easily understand that placing three pulleys in the lower block, and two or three more in the upper, we can multiply the force six times. And if we wish to increase it to any other even number, the pulleys in the lower block are to be numbered according to one-half that number chosen for the multiplication of the force, placing the cord round the pulleys so that one end is fastened to the upper block and the other to the force, as may be easily understood in the accompanying diagram.

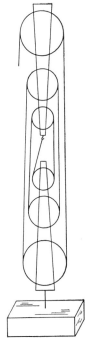

Passing now to the explanation of the method of multiplying the force according to an odd number, and starting with the ratio of one to three, let us first set forth the present theory, upon an understanding of which will depend a knowledge of the entire business at hand.

Let there be the lever AB whose support is A, and from its midpoint C let the heavy body D hang. Let this be supported by two equal forces, one of which is applied at the point C, and the other at the extremity B; then I say that each of these powers has a *moment* equal to the third part of the weight D. For the force at *C* sustains a weight equal to itself, being situated in the same straight line in which the weight *D* hangs and bears down; but the force at *B* sustains twice as much of the weight *D* as itself, its distance from the support *A* (the line *BA*) being double the distance *AC* from which the heavy body is suspended. But since the two forces at *C* and *B* were assumed to be equal to each other, the part of the weight *D* that is sustained by the force *B* is double the part sustained by the force *C*. Hence let the heavy body *D* be made up of two parts, one being double the other, the greater being sustained by the force *B* and the lesser by the force *C*. But this lesser is one-third of the weight *D*; therefore the *moment* of the force *C* is equal to the *moment* of one-third of the weight *D*, and consequently the force *B* will equal this, as we assumed it to be equal to the force *C*. Whence our intention is evident, which was to demonstrate that each of the two powers *C* and *B* is equal to one-third of the weight *D*.

Having demonstrated this, let us get on to the pulleys. Take the lower pulley *ACB*, revolving about the center *G*, from which the weight *H* is suspended, and call the upper pulley *EF*, winding the cord round both as *DFEACBJ*, its end *D* being fastened to the lower block, and the force being applied to the other end *J*. Then I say that the latter, sustaining or moving the weight *H*, will feel but one-third of its heaviness. For considering the structure of this framework, we see the diameter *AB* to serve as a lever whose end *B* receives the force *J*, while the other end *A* serves as fulcrum; from the center *G* is hung the weight *H*, and at the same place another force *D* is applied, so that the weight is held by the three cords *JB*, *FD*, and *EA* which with equal work sustain the weight.

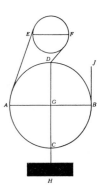

Now by the theory already given, if one of the two equal forces *D* and *B* is applied to the middle of the lever *AB* and the other to its extremity *B*, it is evident that each of these feels only one-third of the weight *H*; therefore the power *J*, having a *moment* equal to one-third of the weight *H*, will be able to sustain and move it. Yet the travel of the force *J* will be triple the path that the weight will take, the force being necessarily prolonged according to the length of the three cords *JB*, *FD*, and *EA*, of which a single one will measure the travel of the weight.

Of the Screw

Among all the mechanical instruments devised by human wit for various conveniences, it seems to me that for ingenuity and utility the screw takes first place, as something cleverly adapted not only to move but also to fix and to press with great force; and it is constructed in such a manner as to occupy but a very small space and yet to accomplish effects that the other instruments could perform only if made into large machines. The screw thus being among the most beautiful and useful of contrivances, we may rightly take the trouble to explain as clearly as we may both its origin and its nature. To do this we shall start from a theory which, though at first it may appear to be somewhat remote from the consideration of this instrument, is nevertheless its basis and foundation.[25]

There can be no doubt that the constitution of nature with respect to the movements of heavy bodies is such that any body which retains heaviness within itself has a propensity, when free, to move toward the center; and not only by a straight perpendicular line, but also, when it cannot do otherwise, along any other line which, having some tilt toward the center, goes downward little by little. And thus we see, for instance, that water from some high place not only drops perpendicularly downward, but also runs about the surface of the earth on lines that are inclined, though but very little. This is seen in the course of rivers whose waters, though the bed is very little slanted, run freely dropping downward; which same effect, just as it is perceived in fluid bodies, appears also in hard solids, provided that their shapes and other external and accidental impediments do not prevent it. So that if we have a surface that is very smooth and polished, as would be that of a mirror, and a perfectly smooth and round ball of marble or glass or some such material capable of being polished, then if this ball is placed on that surface it will go moving along, provided that the surface has some little tilt, even the slightest; and it will remain still only on that surface which is most precisely leveled, and equidistant from the plane of the horizon. This, for example, might be the surface of a frozen lake or pond, upon which such a spherical body would stand still, though with a disposition to be moved by any extremely small force. For we have understood that if such a plane tilted only by

25. The ensuing discussion is of great interest with respect to the history of the fundamental concept which distinguishes modern from ancient physics, that of inertia. It is therefore worth noting that in the earlier version of the *Mechanics* the approach is substantially the same as here, except that instead of going on to derive the rule for equilibrium on the inclined plane, Galileo stops with the remark that the derivation (which he had given in his *De Motu*) is rather complicated, and contents himself with a statement of the result, proceeding immediately then to the analysis of the screw. The fundamental conception involved in inertia, historically at least, is that of the *indifference* of matter to motion and rest. This was taught by Galileo as early as 1593.

a hair, the said ball would move spontaneously toward the lower part, and on the other hand it would have resistance toward the upper or rising part, nor could it be moved that way without some violence. Hence it is perfectly clear that on an exactly balanced surface the ball would remain indifferent and questioning between motion and rest, so that any the least force would be sufficient to move it, just as on the other hand any little resistance, such as that merely of the air that surrounds it, would be capable of holding it still.

From this we may take the following conclusion as an indubitable axiom: That heavy bodies, all external and adventitious impediments being removed, can be moved in the plane of the horizon by any minimum force.[26] But when the same heavy body must be driven upon an ascending plane, having a tendency to the contrary motion and commencing to oppose such an ascent, there will be required greater and greater violence the more elevation the said plane shall have. For example, the movable body *G* being placed on the line *AB* parallel to the horizon, it will stand there, as was said, indifferent to motion or to rest, so that it may be moved by the least force; but if we have the inclined planes *AC*, *AD*, and *AE*, upon these it will be driven only by violence, more of which is required to move it along the line *AD* than along *AC*, and still more along *AE* than *AD*. This comes from its having greater impetus to go downward along the line *EA* than along *DA*, and along *DA* than along *CA*. So that we may likewise conclude heavy bodies to have greater resistance to being moved upon variously inclined planes, according as one is more or less tilted than another; and finally the resistance to being raised will be greatest on the part of the heavy body in the perpendicular *AF*. But what proportion the force must have to

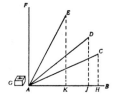

---

26. From the first sentence of this paragraph and the last of the preceding, it would seem that the idea of perpetual continuance of such a body in horizontal motion is a direct implication. But it was a long time before Galileo published even that restricted inertial principle. The idea was certainly formed in his mind and taught to his pupils by 1607, for in April of that year Benedetto Castelli wrote to him: "From Your Excellency's doctrine that although to start motion the mover is necessary, yet to continue it the absence of opposition is sufficient, I find amusement in their exaltation of [Aristotle's] doctrine as making me recognize the existence of God; since if motion had been eternal, I could become an atheist and say that we have no need of God—a dreadful stupidity" (*Opere*, X, 170). In a way it is a pity that Galileo never published his inertial idea in as general a form as his pupil thus ascribed it to him, though in another sense it is a great credit to Galileo as a physicist that he refused to go so far beyond his data to no purpose. Descartes did, being a less cautious physicist than Galileo; and being a more ingenious theologian than Castelli, he managed to derive the general law of inertia from the immovability of God.

the weight in order to draw it upon various inclined planes must
be explained precisely before we proceed further, so that we may
completely understand all that remains to be said.

From the points C, D, and E, therefore, let fall the perpendicu-
lars CH, DJ, and EK upon the horizontal line AB. It will be
demonstrated that the same weight will be moved upon the
inclined plane AC by less force than in the perpendicular AF
(where it will be raised by a force equal to itself), in proportion
as the perpendicular CH is less than AC; and upon the plane AD
the force will have to the weight the same proportion as the
perpendicular line JD has to DA; and finally in the plane AE the
ratio of the force to the weight will be that of KE to EA.

This present theory was attempted also by Pappus of Alexandria in the eighth book of his *Mathematical Collections*, but in
my opinion he missed the mark, being defeated by the assumption which he made when he supposed that the weight would
have to be moved in the horizontal plane by a given force.[27] This
is false, no sensible force being required (neglecting accidental
impediments, which are not considered by the theoretician) to
move the given weight horizontally, so that it is vain thus to seek
the force with which it will be moved on the inclined plane. It
will be better, given the force that would move the object perpendicularly upward (which would equal the weight of the

27. Guido had followed Pappus in this error, and was probably the source of
Galileo's information about it; but Guido being Galileo's patron and friend, it
was more diplomatic here to criticize Pappus. The reasoning which follows in
the text certainly owes nothing to any previous writer. But since we have previously looked at Jordanus' analysis of the inclined plane, let us briefly look also
at those of Pappus and of Guido.

Pappus supposes a sphere of arbitrary size to rest upon an inclined plane. He
connects the center of the sphere to its point of contact, and also by a horizontal
line to the plane; he then draws a vertical line from the point of contact to this
horizontal line. The point of intersection he considers as the fulcrum of a lever,
and placing at the center of the sphere a weight equal to the force supposed to
be required to move the body horizontally, he computes the weight which would
equilibrate this lever if placed on the inclined plane where that is cut by the
horizontal line from the center of the sphere. To this force is then added the
force supposed to be needed to drive the weight horizontally. In effect, this makes
the force required to move the weight up the plane proportional to the square of
the secant of the angle of inclination. This would require an infinite force to lift
any weight vertically, but the early physicists failed to notice such objections,
being enamored of elaborate mathematical "proofs" for their own sake.

Guido, writing on the screw, merely refers to this result of Pappus as the means
of "reduction of the screw to the lever." But in dealing with the use of the wedge
as an inclined plane, he concludes that its power is that of a lever whose fulcrum
is at the point of the wedge. He seems not to notice that this would make a long
wedge more powerful than a short one, or that for a given wedge the mechanical
advantage would be reduced as the weight moved up it, becoming a disadvantage
past the midpoint of the inclined plane.

object), to seek the force that will move it on the inclined plane. This we shall attempt to achieve, with an attack different from that of Pappus.

Consider, then, the circle *AJC* and in this the diameter *ABC* with center *B*, and two weights of equal *moments* at the extremi-

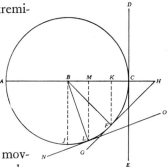

ties *A* and *C*, so that the line *AC* being a lever or balance movable about the center *B*, the weight *C* will be sustained by the weight *A*. But if we imagine the arm of the balance *BC* to be inclined downward along the line *BF* in such a way that the two lines *AB* and *BF* are fixed together at the point *B*, then the *moment* of the weight *C* will no longer be equal to the *moment* of the weight *A*, the distance of the point *F* from the line *BJ*, which goes from the support *B* to the center of the earth, being diminished.

Now if we draw from the point *F* a perpendicular to *BC*, which is *FK*, the *moment* of the weight at *F* will be as if it were hung from the line *KB*; and as the distance *KB* is made smaller with respect to the distance *BA*, the *moment* of the weight *F* is accordingly diminished from the *moment* of the weight *A*.[28] Likewise, as the weight inclines more, as along the line *BL*, its *moment* will go on diminishing, and it will be as if it were hung from the distance *BM* along the line *ML*, in which point *L* a weight placed at *A* will sustain one as much less than itself as the distance *BA* is greater than the distance *BM*.

You see, then, how the weight placed at the end of the line *BC*, inclining downward along the circumference *CFLJ*, comes gradually to diminish its *moment* and its impetus to go downward, being sustained more and more by the lines *BF* and *BL*. But to consider this heavy body as descending and sustained now less and now more by the radii *BF* and *BL*, and as constrained to travel along the circumference *CFL*, is not different from imagining the same circumference *CFLJ* to be a surface of the same curvature placed under the same movable body, so that this body, being supported upon it, would be constrained to descend

28. Galileo does not deal with the bent lever separately, but this discussion affords a basis for the quantitative analysis of that problem.

along it. For in either case the movable body traces out the same path, and it does not matter whether it is suspended from the center B and sustained by the radius of the circle, or whether this support is removed and it is supported by and travels upon the circumference $CFLJ$. Whence we may undoubtedly affirm that the heavy body descending from the point C along the circumference $CFLJ$, its *moment* of descent at the first point C is total and integral, since it is in no way supported by the circumference; and at this first point C it has no disposition to move differently from what it would freely do in the perpendicular tangent DCE. But if the movable body is located at the point F, then its heaviness is partly sustained by the circular path placed under it, and its *moment* downward is diminished in that proportion by which the line BK is exceeded by the line BC. Now when the movable body is at F, at the first point of its motion it is as if it were on an inclined plane according to the tangent line GFH, since the tilt of the circumference at the point F does not differ from the tilt of the tangent FG, apart from the insensible angle of contact.[29]

And in the same way we shall find that at the point L the *moment* of the same movable body is diminished as the line BM is diminished from BC, so that in the tangent plane to the circle at L, represented by the line NLO, the *moment* of descent is lessened in the movable body in the same proportion. Therefore if on the plane HG the *moment* of the movable body is diminished from its total impetus (which it has in the perpendicular DCE) in the proportion of the line KB to the line BC or BF, the similarity of the triangles KBF and KFH making the proportion between the lines KF and FH the same as between KB and BF, we conclude that the whole and absolute *moment* that the movable body has in the perpendicular to the horizon is in the same proportion to that which it has on the inclined plane HF as the line HF is to the line FK, which is that of the length of the inclined plane to the perpendicular dropped from this on the

29. This analysis of the components of forces in descent along a circle, rich in mathematical insight, is almost the precise reverse of Guido's attempted account of the loss of apparent weight in various positions on a circle. Guido considers the radius drawn to the weight as lending support to it, so that the apparent weight diminishes in proportion to the angle between that radius and the line drawn from the weight to the center of the earth (*Le Mechaniche*, ff. 10r.–11r.). Galileo's analysis of constrained circular motion into successive tangential motions later enabled him to make the first significant contribution to the study of centrifugal force; see *Opere*, VII, 242–44 (*Dialogue*, pp. 215–17). It should also be noted that the analysis used here suggests that he had already associated the pendulum with the inclined plane.

horizontal. So that, passing to the present separate diagram, the *moment* downward of the movable body on the inclined plane *FH* has the same proportion to the total *moment* with which it presses down in the perpendicular *FK* as this line *KF* has to *FH*. This being the case, it is clear that the force that sustains the weight on the perpendicular *FK* must be equal to the weight, so that to sustain it on the inclined plane *FH* there will suffice one as much less than that as this perpendicular *FK* is less than the line *FH*. And since, as has been mentioned at other times, the force to move the weight need only insensibly exceed that which sustains it, we derive this general conclusion: That upon the inclined plane the force has the same proportion to the weight as the perpendicular dropped to the horizontal from the end of the plane has to the length of the plane.[30]

Returning now to our original purpose, which was to investigate the nature of the screw, let us consider the triangle *ACB*, of which the line *AB* is horizontal, *BC* is perpendicular to it, and *AC* is the inclined plane upon which the movable body *D* will be drawn by a force as much less than itself as the line *BC* is shorter

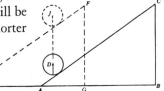

than *CA*. Now to raise the same weight on the same plane *AC* with the triangle *CAB* standing still and the weight *D* being moved toward *C*, is the same thing as if the weight *D* were not moved from the perpendicular *DJ* while the triangle was being driven forward toward *H*, for when the triangle has reached the place *FHG* the movable body will have climbed to the altitude *AJ*.[31]

Now finally the form and first essence of the screw is no other than such a triangle *ACB* which, driven forward, slips under the heavy body to be raised, and boosts it or jacks it up (as they say); and such was its first origin. Whoever was its first inventor

30. By reducing the analysis of force on the inclined plane to the vertical component, Galileo utilizes the true principle of virtual velocities; and not only that, but his previous reduction of circular to tangential motions, as also the utilization of insensible forces in his analysis, introduces in effect the use of infinitesimal displacements in place of gross motions. The ancient notions of equality or proportionality of large displacements, without strict consideration of the directions of action of forces, scarcely merit the name of physical principles.

31. Guido had previously described the driving of a wedge in this way as equivalent to moving the weight up an inclined plane, but he went completely astray in considering the upper surface of the wedge as a lever. See note 27, above.

considered that as the triangle *ABC* coming forward raised the weight *D,* so an instrument could be constructed similar to the said triangle of some solid material which, driven forward, would elevate the given weight; but then considering better how such a machine could be reduced to a much smaller and more convenient form, he took the same triangle and wound it round the cylinder *ABCD* in such a manner that the altitude *CB* of the triangle should be the height of the cylinder. Thus the ascending plane generates upon the cylinder the helical line denoted by the line *AEFGH,* which is commonly called the thread of the screw; and in this way there was created the instrument called by the Greeks *cochlea,* and by us the screw; which, turning round, comes to bear with its thread beneath the weight and easily raises it.

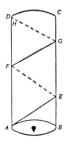

Now having demonstrated that upon the inclined plane the force has to the weight the same proportion as the perpendicular height of the inclined plane has to its length, we thus understand that the force is multiplied by the screw *ABCD* according to the ratio that the length of its entire thread *AEFGH* has to its height *CB.* In this way we learn that the more dense the threading of the screw by its helices, the more powerful it becomes, as being generated by a less steeply inclined plane, whose length is in greater proportion to its own perpendicular height. But let us not neglect to mention that if we wish to find the force of a given screw we do not have to measure the length of its entire thread, and the height of its whole cylinder, but it will suffice that we examine the number of times the distance between any two contiguous elements divides a single revolution of the thread. This, for example, will be the number of times the distance *AF* is contained in the length of the turn *AEF,* for this is the same proportion that the entire height *CB* has to the whole thread.

When one understands all we have said about the nature of this instrument, I do not doubt that all its other properties can be understood without trouble—as, for instance, that instead of raising the weight upon the screw, a female thread is accommodated to it with a concave helix in which the male thread of the screw enters and is then turned round, raising and lifting this nut together with the weight attached to it.

Finally one must not ignore the consideration which from the beginning has been said to hold for all mechanical instruments, that is, that whatever is gained in force by their means is lost in time and in speed. Perhaps to someone this may not appear so clearly in the present instance, and it may even seem that the force is multiplied without the mover traveling farther than the body moved. For let us suppose in the triangle *ABC* the line *AB* to be horizontal, *AC* to be the inclined plane whose height is measured by the perpendicular *CB*, and a movable body to be placed on the plane *AC*, and linked by the cord *EDF* to a force

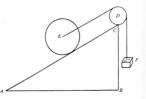

or weight placed at *F*. Then if its proportion to the heaviness of the weight *E* is the same as that of the line *BC* to *CA*, from what has been proven, the weight *F* will descend, drawing the movable body *E* along the inclined plane without the weight *F* measuring a greater space in descending than the movable body *E* measures along the line *AC*. But here it should be noticed that although the movable body *E* will have passed over all the line *AC* in the same time that the other heavy body *F* will have fallen through an equal interval, nevertheless the heavy body *E* will not have been removed from the common center of heavy things more than the distance along the perpendicular *CB*, while the heavy body *F* descending perpendicularly will have dropped by a space equal to the whole line *AC*. And since heavy bodies do not have any resistance to transverse motions except in proportion to their removal from the center of the earth,[32] then the movable body *E* not being raised more than the distance *CB* in the whole motion *AC*, while *F* has dropped perpendicularly as much as the whole length of *AC*, we may rightly say that the travel of the force *F* has the same ratio to the travel of the force *E* as the line *AC* has to the line *CB*, or as the weight *E* has to the weight *F*. Therefore it is very important to consider along what lines the motions are made, and especially of inanimate heavy bodies, whose *moments* have their whole power and their entire resistance in the line perpendicular to the horizon; and in other lines, transversely rising or falling, they have only that power, impetus, or resistance which is greater or lesser according as the inclinations approach more or less to the perpendicular elevation.

Of the Archimedean Screw for Raising Water

I should not pass over in silence here the invention of Archimedes for raising water, which is not only marvelous, but miraculous; for we shall find that the water ascends in a screw

---

32. The importance of this observation must not be overlooked; it contains the essential basis of the principle of virtual work, here related by the context to Galileo's limited inertial principle. The remainder of this paragraph affords a theoretical basis for analyzing all static forces in terms of weights.

continually descending. But before going further, let us explain the use of this screw in the raising of water.

Consider in the next diagram the column *MJKH* with the winding line *JLOPQRSH* round it, which is a channel through which water may run. If we place the end *J* in water, tilting the

screw as shown in the figure, and then turn it about the two pivots *T* and *V*, the water will go running through the channel until it finally pours out at the mouth *H*. Now I say that the water descends continually in being conducted from the point *J* to the point *H*, although *H* is higher than *J*. How this may be, we shall explain in the following way.

Let us describe the triangle *ACB*, by which the screw *JH* is generated, so that the channel of the screw is represented by the line *AC*, whose rise and elevation is determined by the angle *CAB*. That is, if this angle shall be one-third or one-fourth of a right angle, the elevation of the channel *AC* will be according to the third or fourth part of a right angle. Now it is clear that the rise of this channel *AC* will be taken away if the point *C* is dropped to *B*, for then the channel *AC* will have no elevation at all, and dropping the point *C* a little below *B*, the water would naturally run out downward through the channel *AC* from the point *A* to the point *C*. Thus we conclude that if the angle *A* is one-third of a right angle, the rise of the channel would be completely removed if the part *C* were dropped through one-third of a right angle.

These things understood, let us turn the triangle round the column, and let us make the screw *BAEFGHJD*. If placed upright at right angles with the extremity *B* in water, this would not upon being turned round draw up the water, since the channel about the column would be elevated as seen by the part *BA*. But even though the column stood upright and at right angles,

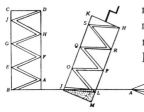

the rise through the screw twisted round the column would not thereby be of greater elevation than one-third of a right angle, the rise being generated by the elevation of the channel *AD*. Hence if we tilt the column through one-third of a right angle and a little more, as is seen in *JKHM,* the course and motion through the channel will no longer be elevated, but depressed, as seen in the channel *JL;* therefore the water will move downward from the point *J* to the point *L.* And turning the screw round, its various parts successively displace one another and present themselves to the water in the same position as the part *JL,* whence the water will go continually descending, and yet eventually it will be found to have climbed from the point *J* to the point *H;* and what a marvelous thing this is, I leave him to judge who has completely understood it. But from what has been said, one will know why the water-raising screw must be tilted a little more than the degree of the triangle by which the screw is described.

Of the Force of Percussion

To investigate what is the cause of the force of percussion is most necessary for many reasons. First, because in this there appears to be something much more marvelous than that which is perceived in any other mechanical instrument; for when a nail is struck to fix it in some very hard wood, or a stick that must penetrate into very firm ground, each is driven forward by the force of the percussion alone; without which, if we were to place the hammer on either, it would not move, nor would it do so even if a much heavier weight than the hammer were so placed.[33] This effect is truly marvelous, and is the more worthy of speculation in my opinion because, so far as I know, none of those who have philosophized about it before us has hit the mark, which we may take as a certain and sure sign of the obscurity and difficulty of such speculation. For as to Aristotle and others who have tried to reduce the cause of this remarkable effect to the length of the handle of the hammer, it seems to me that without any long argument one can expose the weakness of their reasoning by the effect of those instruments which, without having any handle, give percussion either by falling from on high or by being driven speedily from the side.[34] Therefore we must have recourse to

33. *Mechanical Problems,* sec. 19: "Why is it that if one puts a large axe on a block of wood and a heavy weight on top of it, it does not cut the wood to any extent; but if one raises the axe and strikes with it, it splits it in half, even if the striker has far less weight than one placed on it and pressing it down? Is it because all work is produced by movement, and a heavy object produces the movement of weight more when it is moving than when it is at rest?"

34. It is not quite fair to attribute this remark to Aristotle, or even to the Aristotelian writer of the *Mechanical Problems,* whose reference to long handles was made in quite another connection (sec. 13). It was Guido who introduced

some other principle if we want to find the truth of this matter. And though the cause is by its nature somewhat abstruse and difficult to explain, yet we shall attempt with as much lucidity as we can command to render it clear and palpable, showing in the end that the basis and origin of the effect derives from no other source than that from which the causes of other mechanical effects have sprung.

Now this will be done by keeping before our eyes that which has been seen to happen in all other mechanical operations, which is that the force, the resistance, and the space through which the motion is made respectively follow that proportion and obey those laws by which a resistance equal to the force will be moved by this force through an equal space and with equal velocity to that of the mover. Likewise, a force that is one-half of a resistance will be able to move it, provided the former moves with double the velocity, or let us say through twice as great a distance, as that passed through by the resistance moved. And in brief, it is seen in all other instruments that any great resistance may be moved by any given little force, provided that the space through which this force is moved shall have to the space through which the resistance shall be moved that proportion which exists between this large resistance and the small force; and this is by the necessary constitution of nature. Whence, turning the argument about and arguing by the converse, where will be the marvel if that power which would move a small resistance through a large interval should drive one a hundred times greater through one-hundredth of the said interval? No wonder, certainly; and for things to be otherwise would be not only absurd, but impossible.[35]

We shall consider, therefore, the resistance to being moved that exists in the hammer at the point where it goes to strike, and how far it would be driven by the received force if it did not strike; and moreover what is the resistance to being moved of that which it strikes, and how much it is moved by a single

---

this idea explicitly, deducing it from a general rule used in the Aristotelian work (*Le Mechaniche*, ff. 113v.–114r.).

35. This bold application of a general principle of physics obtained by induction led Galileo close to a solution of the problem; but in his attempt to measure the moving force he became ensnared in difficulties, as the next paragraph discloses. In later years he came to regard the force of percussion as infinite, but he never completed and published his researches, which in their unfinished form make up the so-called sixth day intended for the *Two New Sciences* (*Opere*, VIII, 321–46).

stroke. And having found how far this great resistance goes forward under one stroke, by however much this is less than the distance through which the hammer would go by the impetus (*empito*) of what moves it, by so much is this resistance greater than that of the hammer; and so the wonder of the effect ceases in us, since it stems only from the terms of natural arrangements and from what has already been said.[36]

Let there be added, for better comprehension, an example in particular terms. There is a hammer which, having four of resistance, is moved by a force such that if it were set free from this at that point where the stroke is made, it would go ten paces beyond if it met with no obstruction. But let it rather be opposed there by a great beam whose resistance to motion is as four thousand; that is, one thousand times as great as that of the hammer (and yet not immovable, so that it would overcome the resistance of the hammer beyond all proportion). Now the percussion being made on this, it will indeed be driven forward, but by the thousandth part of the ten paces in which the hammer would be moved. And thus, reflecting with a converse method that which has been theorized on other mechanical effects, we may investigate the cause of the force of percussion.[37]

I know that this will give rise in some to difficulties and objec-

36. The "resistance to being moved" is certainly a primitive mass concept, which Galileo avoids measuring in terms of weight because he is contemplating horizontal motion. The next concept, however, presents real difficulties. How far would the hammer go if set free? Galileo seems to have been thinking only of the empirical fact that a thrown hammer will fall to the ground at a distance somehow proportional to the force given it by the thrower. It is curious that he did not revert to the idea of velocity here, as in the discussion of the steelyard, especially after having remarked that no force is required to carry a body horizontally.

37. The attempt to supply a model calculation only makes matters worse. But considering that Galileo was not given to circulating in writing conjectures that were devoid of internal consistency in his mind, let us attempt to reconstruct a possible line of thought he may have followed.

The hammer is given four units of resistance; that is, of some property which also exists and can be measured in the other object that is to be moved. Hence in saying that the hammer will go ten paces if unobstructed, he ought to have considered it as moving this hypothetical distance under conditions similar to those governing the thing struck. If he did so, we may forgive him his utter incapacity to specify such conditions, as he seems to have been considering a large beam resting on the ground. And for theoretical purposes he now had a legitimate work concept. But it is unfortunate that he did not take both his beam and his hammer off the ground and suspend them in trusses, or place them on his frictionless frozen lake, in which case he would have been forced to remove the ambiguities and contradictions in his exposition; and if it then did not result in what he set out to accomplish, we might have had from him instead a discussion of the laws of impact.

tions, which however there are means to remove with little trouble, and these we willingly leave among the mechanical problems which will be appended at the end of this discourse.[38]

38. The *Problems of Mechanics* here promised by Galileo have never been found.

Appendix

An Extract from the "Mechanics Taught at Padua in 1594"[1]

On Compound Instruments
Chapter 16

Since thus far the particular instruments and their nature have been explained, we wish to show their *multiplication and* composition, and the multiplication of wheels that was discovered by Archimedes,[2] which was as follows.

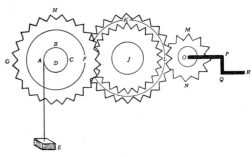

First let there be the axle *ABC* around the center and support *D,* about which axle is wound the *cord* that sustains the weight [*E*], and for the revolving and turning of *this axis with* less work

1. In the ensuing extracts, which comprise the sections of Galileo's lectures on mechanics that were omitted from the later circulated text, the body of the text follows the Ratisbon copy published by Favaro. Italicized words give readings based upon the Pasadena copy, and words enclosed in square brackets are conjectural emendations by the translator.

2. Plutarch's story of the powerful machine used by Archimedes has it composed of pulleys, but other traditions made it depend upon levers or upon trains of gears. Stevin, like Galileo, ascribed to Archimedes the machine given by Hero under the name of *Baroulkos*. See *Principal Works*, I, 355 ff.

let us put to it the wheel *GHF*, and *it is evident* by the nature of
the axle in the wheel[3] that *with this* single wheel the force is
multiplied according to the ratio of the radius *of the wheel FD to
the radius* of the axle *DA*. But if we now want to add a second
wheel [*KL*], let us fit out another axle *J*, which when turned
round will rotate the wheel *GHF*, for which purpose teeth will
be made for this and for the said wheel *D*. Then to be able to
turn the axle *J* easily, let us place it in the *second* wheel *KL*,
which turned, sets in motion the axle *J* with as much less work as
the radius of the wheel *KL* is greater than the radius of the axle
J, and thus we shall have the second multiplication of force; and
in the same order we may add as many wheels as we please;
and finally to move the last wheel *KL*, let us add another toothed
wheel, or let us call it gear, *MNL*, whose teeth shall correspond
to those of the wheel *KL*. *And* to set this last gear *MN* turning
let us add the iron crank *OPQR* in such a way that by placing
our hand on the handle *QR* we may turn the gear *MN* with as
much less work as the line *PQ* is greater than the radius of the
gear; for the line *PQ*, being rotated, is drawn by a circle or wheel
described from the point *O*, which with the gear *NM* makes the
same instrument as the axle in the wheel; and this is the third
multiplication.

It remains now for us to explain the method of computing and
calculating the force of the whole instrument, which may be
deduced from the ratios of the radii of the wheels with respect to
the radii of the gears; thus, for example, if the radius of the first
wheel *FD* is five times the radius of the axle *DA*, one-fifth of the
force placed at *F* will move the weight. And with the gear *J*
added, consider how much greater the radius of the second wheel
is than the radius of the gear *J*; suppose it to be four times as
large, then one-fourth of the force *required at* the point *F* will
suffice at the point *L*. But the point *F* needs one-fifth of the force;
therefore one-twentieth will be enough at the point *L*.

Finally, considering how much greater the distance *PQ* is than
the radius of the gear *OL*, in that proportion will the force be
diminished; and supposing it three times as large, one-third of
the force that was necessary at the point *L* will suffice at the point
Q; but the force *at L* has been demonstrated to be one-twentieth
of the weight; therefore one-sixtieth will suffice at the point *Q*.
And with this reasoning we shall proceed to any other multiplication of wheels.

3. This phrase has been translated "windlass" in the foregoing text.

It remains for us to demonstrate that the force at Q is moved through a space *sixty times* as great as the space through which the weight is moved, which we shall *deduce* with such reasoning: It was assumed at the beginning that the radius FD was five times the radius DA, from which it follows that the circumference of the wheel GHF is *similarly five* times the circumference of the axle ABC; if therefore *we know* the axle ABC to have a circuit of one braccio,[4] the circumference of the wheel GHF will be five braccia, and when the axle ABC shall have turned once [and] the weight as a consequence *will have* risen one braccio, the force placed at F will have moved through a space of five braccia. Next let us suppose the circumference of the gear J to be for example one-half braccio, and since the circumference GHF *has been supposed as five braccia, when that circumference GHF* shall have made one turn, the gear J will have made *ten,* and the *entire* wheel KL as many. *And* since the circumference KL is four times the circumference of the gear J (having a circuit of two braccia, that is), it has been said that in the time that the axle ABC shall have made one turn and the weight shall have risen one braccio, the wheel KL will have made ten, and the force *in* it will have moved through a space of twenty braccia. Now let the circumference of the gear MN be, for example, another half braccio; the circumference of KL being two braccia, when the latter shall have made ten turns, and the axle ABC one, the gear MN and the force *applied at Q* will have made forty. And since the circle described from the point Q is said to be three times as large as the circumference of the gear MN, which is one-half braccio, the said circumference *from* the point Q will be one and one-half braccia; whence the force *applied to* this *in* forty revolutions will be moved through the space of sixty braccia; and *in* such time the weight, as was said, will have risen one braccio. You see, then, that *in* this instrument also the same proportion is derived, and it increases *in* slowness as the work is diminished.

Of the Perpetual Screw[5]

Chapter 17

It is customary to join and compound three instruments together with an ingenious artifice; that is, the axle in the wheel, the screw, and the capstan; and this compound is called the perpetual screw for the reason we shall give below, after we have

4. A *braccio* (plural *braccia*) was approximately 22 inches.
5. This compound machine was also discussed by Guido,

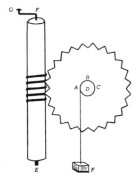

shown its composition. And first, arranging the axle of the wheel *ABC* as in the next diagram, the axle *D,* and wheel *ABC,* and the teeth of the latter, next take a *part of a* screw whose threads are fitted together with the teeth of the [wheel *ABC*].[6]

It is evident that the screw being turned, and *the* teeth of the wheel entering between one *thread* and another, the wheel will also commence to turn, and *one* tooth *slipping in* after another in the threads, there comes to *be made* a perpetual motion; that is, without ever ending *we may* with the same screw make *the wheel* turn continually. From which effect this comes to be called the perpetual screw. Besides this, in order to set the screw turning there will be added the bar *FG* in resemblance to the motion of the capstan, whereby the force being placed *at G,* and turned round, the screw will come to move, *and* the screw will move the wheel, *and* the wheel will move the axle, and the axle will raise the weight. And if we want to calculate the multiplication of the force of all this instrument, let us proceed part by part. Finding, for example, *that* the radius of the wheel is five times that of the radius of the axle, with the wheel alone the fifth part of the force will raise the weight; the screw added, let us note (as was explained before) how much greater one entire revolution of the thread is than the interval between one thread and another; this being, for example, ten times, the force will be multiplied tenfold; whence, one-fifth of the force sufficing with the wheel alone, with the addition of the screw one-fiftieth will be enough; and finally coming to the bar, let us see how many times greater the distance *FG* is than the radius of the screw; and with that proportion let us multiply the force, so that (for example) the distance *FG* being four times the radius of the screw, with the addition of this bar one two-hundredth of the force will suffice.

6. Both texts here incorrectly repeat the words "screw *FE.*"

Index

Index

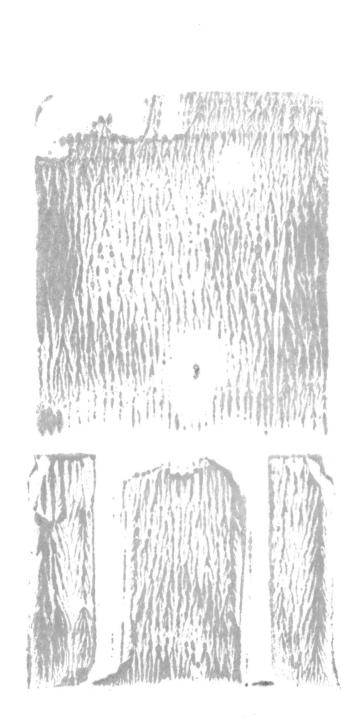